T210
Environmental control and public health

The Open (

Block 4
Wastes management

This publication forms part of an Open University course T210 Environmental Control and Public Health. Details of this and other Open University courses can be obtained from the Student Registration and Enquiry Service, The Open University, PO Box 197, Milton Keynes MK7 6BJ, United Kingdom: tel. +44 (0)845 300 60 90, email general-enquiries@open.ac.uk

Alternatively, you may visit the Open University website at http://www.open.ac.uk where you can learn more about the wide range of courses and packs offered at all levels by The Open University.

To purchase a selection of Open University course materials visit http://www.ouw.co.uk, or contact Open University Worldwide, Michael Young Building, Walton Hall, Milton Keynes MK7 6AA, United Kingdom for a brochure. tel. +44 (0)1908 858793; fax +44 (0)1908 858787; email ouw-customer-services@open.ac.uk

This course has been printed on Savannah Natural Art™: at least 60% of the fibre used in the production of this paper is bagasse (the fibrous residue of sugar cane, left after the sugar has been extracted) and the balance is softwood fibre which has undergone an oxygen bleaching process.

The Open University
Walton Hall, Milton Keynes
MK7 6AA

First published 2002. Second edition 2003. Third edition 2007

Edited and designed by The Open University.

Typeset by SR Nova Pvt. Ltd, Bangalore, India.

Printed and bound in the United Kingdom by Hobbs the Printers, Brunel Road, Totton, Hampshire.

ISBN 978 0 7492 2411 0

3.1

T210 Course Team

Dr Suresh Nesaratnam	course chair/author
Judith Anderson	course manager
Dr Rod Barratt	author
Sylvan Bentley	picture researcher
Philippa Broadbent	print buying controller
Dr Stephen Burnley	author
Roger Busby	author
Dr Keith Cavanagh	author/editor
Dr Sally Crompton	author
Jim Frederickson	author
Pam Furniss	author
Keith Horton	external consultant/author
Caryl Hunter-Brown	subject information specialist
Dr Alan Kirkwood	external consultant/author
Jo Lambert	learning projects manager
Roy Lawrance	graphic artist
Karen Lemmon	compositor
Vicki McCulloch	graphic designer
James McLannahan	consultant
Katie Meade	rights executive
Dr Dick Morris	consultant
Dr John Newbury	consultant
Stewart Nixon	software developer
Dr Julian Parfitt	author
Dr Shirley Payne	consultant
Dr Michael Peet	BBC (OU Production Centre)
Prof. Andrew Porteous	consultant
Janice Robertson	editor
Dr David Sharp	consultant
Dr Shahram Taherzadeh	author
Mark Thomas	software developer
Marjorie Thompson	course secretary
Dr James Warren	author
Rob Westcott	editor

In addition the Course Team wishes to thank the following for reviewing the material:

External assessor	Prof. Douglas Probert
Block 2	Jenny Morris
Block 3	Prof. Hugh Tebbutt, Cynthia Blackwell
Block 4	Dr Jan Gronow, Pat Wheeler, Dr Derek Lohmann
Block 5	Oliver Hetherington
Block 6	Michael Gittins
Block 7	Brian Price

Contents of the course

CONTENTS

LEARNING OUTCOMES

The aims of this block are:

■ to give you an appreciation of the impacts on public health and on the wider environment of the collection, treatment and final disposal of solid wastes produced in the UK;

■ to examine ways in which wastes can be managed in order to minimize any adverse health and environmental impacts;

■ to review the ways in which European and national waste policy and legislation influence the waste management options and technologies adopted in the UK;

■ to examine ways in which materials and energy can be recovered from wastes.

Knowledge and awareness

After studying this block and the relevant entries in the Set Book and Legislation Supplement, watching the associated DVD programmes, and conducting the home experiments you should have acquired knowledge and awareness of:

1   the types and quantities of wastes produced in the UK by the commercial, industrial and domestic sectors (SAQs 1, 4, 5);

2   the legislative and regulatory frameworks that govern wastes management in the UK (SAQs 2, 9, 19, 33);

3   the principal methods of treating and disposing of wastes, and the technology behind each method;

4   the scientific and technological principles behind waste management processes and pollution prevention/abatement methods (SAQs 16, 17, 25);

5   the cost of the different waste management options (SAQs 6, 21, 28, 29, 30, 31);

6   the principles and application of integrated waste management and how such a system may be devised (SAQ 15);

7   the methods for managing hazardous wastes and how these differ from municipal wastes management (SAQs 32–9, 53);

8   the occurrence and treatment of contaminated land in the UK and the risks that contaminated land presents (SAQs 53, 54);

9   the basic principle of radioactive decay (and you should be able to distinguish between the principal radioactive decay processes) (SAQs 40–43);

10   the significance of, and calculation of, half-life (SAQs 44, 51);

11   how radioactivity can affect human health (SAQs 46, 49);

12   the significance of ionizing radiation and linear energy transfer (SAQ 47);

13   the major sources of radioactivity in the environment (SAQ 50).

Thinking (cognitive) skills

After studying this block you should have the skills to:

14 use information on the composition of municipal and other solid wastes to calculate the potential for the recovery of materials, compost and energy from different wastes (SAQs 1, 4, 5, 7, 14, 15, 18, 19, 20, 22, 24);

15 quantify the main sources of industrial and commercial waste and compare the similarities and differences between these materials and municipal solid waste (SAQs 7, 10, 11, 19);

16 define the term 'hazardous waste' and understand the criteria for deciding whether a particular waste should be classed as a hazardous waste (SAQs 8, 9 11, 33, 53);

17 quantify ways in which the business and domestic sectors could reduce the amount of waste they produce and reuse waste materials (SAQs 6, 27, 28);

18 discuss the health and environmental implications of waste recycling and recovery options (SAQs 3, 10, 31);

19 describe and evaluate the designs of, and processes carried out in:

    municipal and hazardous waste landfill sites (SAQs 3, 12, 13);

    municipal and hazardous waste incinerators (SAQs 15, 16, 35, 36);

    anaerobic digestion and composting processes (SAQs 18, 25, 26);

    materials reclamation facilities (MRFs) (SAQs 20, 23);

20 appraise techniques used in each of the above processes to minimize harm to public health and the environment (SAQs 12, 13, 17, 23, 32, 34);

21 critically discuss dose–response models for radiation (SAQs 48, 49);

22 critically discuss the main methods of radioactive waste disposal (SAQ 52).

Professional and practical skills

In addition, you will have acquired several new skills:

23 using the World Wide Web to obtain information on national and local waste management strategies and plans;

24 carrying out household waste surveys and analysing the resulting data (home experiments);

25 testing composts using bioassay tests (home experiments).

1   INTRODUCTION

1.1   What is waste?

Before we begin this block, we need to answer a very important and fundamental question: 'What is waste?' It is unlikely that different people would come up with the same answer to this question. This is because our environments influence the views we hold about waste. For example, my children (aged 11 and 8) gave the following answers:

> What we produce and throw away: things we don't need.

and

> Rubbish and stuff that people don't want.

The European framework directive on waste, which sets out the EU's position, states that waste is:

> any substance or object which the holder disposes of or is required to dispose of pursuant to the provisions of national law in force

> > Council of the European Communities (1975)

On the face of it, these three definitions are all saying the same thing – 'something that someone throws away' – so all should be clear. But is it? Consider the following example. A scrap metal dealer buys scrap metal from one firm and processes it in some way; perhaps by reducing the pieces to a uniform size, screening out the fine material and finally sorting the metal into different types or grades of alloy. The dealer then sells the sorted alloys to a smelting firm to be made into new goods. Is the scrap metal dealer handling a 'waste' and should this process be subject to the various waste regulations? This question was the subject of a long dispute between the Environment Agency and one of the UK's largest scrap metal merchants through the courts. Eventually the case reached the High Court which ruled that the scrap metal is a waste if the original owner intends to dispose of it and the new owner has to process the material (for example by sorting, crushing or baling) before it can be used (for example by a steelworks or non-ferrous metal manufacturer). The fact that the merchant paid for the scrap was not considered relevant; the scrap was classed as 'waste' because the firm that produced the scrap wanted to dispose of it.

The whole question of defining waste is a complex subject and will almost certainly be the subject of many more legal challenges in the future. This is not something you need to worry about too much in T210, but you should be aware that it is a contentious issue.

For most of T210 we can take a more general standpoint and consider waste to be:

> the unwanted outputs from a system or activity.

Figure 1 shows the inputs and outputs from a typical household. All these outputs can be considered to be wastes. You should also note that wastes are not just solids; the exhaust gases from the boiler and the liquids discharged to the sewer are also wastes. If we define wastes as all 'unwanted outputs' we can also include the energy rejected in the boiler gases and the noise generated by day-to-day activities.

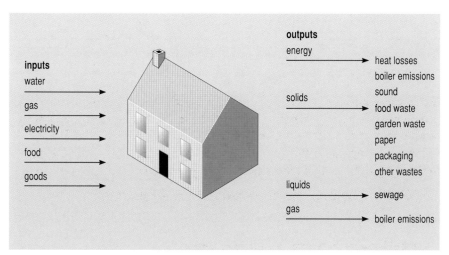

Figure 1   Major household inputs and outputs

Models such as that shown in Figure 1 are a useful way of identifying wastes. These models can be developed into what are known as 'mass balances'. A mass balance quantifies the mass of every material entering each input stream, the mass of material (by type) in each output stream and the mass of any materials accumulating in the system. This is often done for individual industrial processes. (See Figure 103 in the Set Book entry on *incineration*. This shows a mass balance of a modern municipal waste incinerator, which we will be considering in detail in Chapter 9.)

It is also possible to produce mass balances for entire offices, factories or even whole communities. The organization Biffaward used funding from *landfill tax* sources to finance a project carried out by Best Foot Forward and Imperial College to calculate the *ecological footprint* for the Isle of Wight. As an island community, much of the island's food and all its other resources (goods, energy, raw materials) need to be imported. This study showed that, if the whole of the world's population shared the consumption patterns of the island's residents, two-and-a-half planets would be required to provide the resources consumed. The first stage in this calculation was to determine a mass balance for the island, as shown in Figure 2.

SAQ 1

List some of the terms you use in your household to describe things that are really wastes.

In this block we are concerned with the solid wastes that have the greatest potential for causing damage to human health or harm to the wider environment: municipal, commercial, construction and demolition, and industrial wastes. These are known as 'controlled wastes' and they include specialized types of waste such as hazardous wastes, healthcare waste, agricultural waste (excluding manures and crop residues) and contaminated land. The handling, treatment and disposal of controlled wastes are all tightly regulated. Controlled wastes are defined fully in the Legislation Supplement. Together they form the main focus for the remainder of this block.

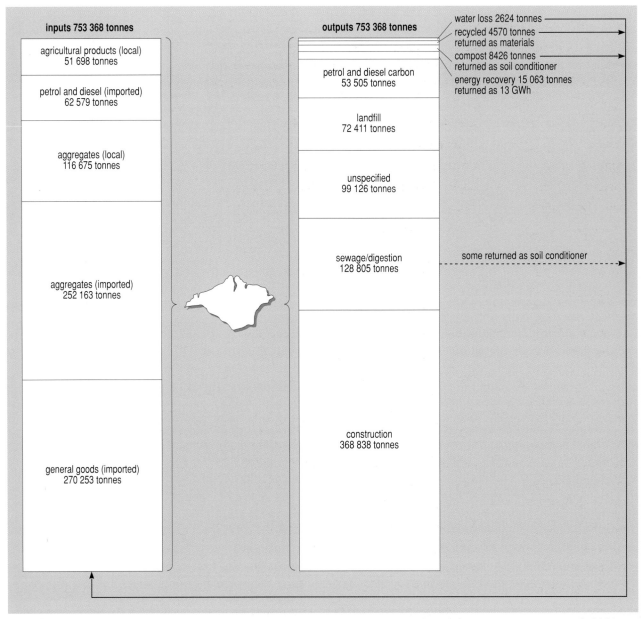

Figure 2   Mass balance input/output diagram for the Isle of Wight (source: adapted from Best Foot Forward, 2001, Figure 3, p.18)

However, there are also several other waste streams that you also need to be aware of, in particular:

- wastes arising from wastewater treatment;

- radioactive wastes;

- wastes from mining and quarrying.

These other waste streams are collectively known as 'non-controlled wastes'; you have already met the first of these in Block 3: *Water pollution control*. Wastes from mining and quarrying are mentioned briefly but are outside the scope of this course.

WASTE BY ANY OTHER NAME

Industry and commerce are major producers of waste, but wastes are nothing to be proud of. Not surprisingly, many organizations have developed a whole range of euphemisms to hide the fact that they generate more waste than they would like to admit to.

scrap	tank loss	rubbish
rejects	cleaning loss	refuse
returns	excess stock	garbage
losses	contamination	trash
material variances	damage	downgraded
broken	moisture content	credits
tails	cleavage loss	dust
end of run	over-make	core loss
set up loss	swarf	slab off
residue	non-standard	deckle loss
allowance	yield loss	consumables
overfill	make ups	evaporation
stock loss	give away	samples
stock adjustments	hidden loss	trials
side runs	extraction	washings
trim	batch growth	over issue
salvage	cross-contamination	factory shop
unavoidable losses	dipstick error	sweepings
geometric losses	over-specification	dross
rework	unauthorized use	shortages
under-delivery	shrinkage	seconds
obsolete stock	standards	overweight
industry standard	leakage	defects
spillage	cancelled order	process loss
packaging	sludge	

1.2 A historical perspective

Humans have produced waste for as long as our species has existed, but people only became aware of wastes when agriculture began to develop and the nomadic hunter-gatherers became more settled. In the early stages of human settlements waste was not a major problem; most of it could be used as an animal feed (food scraps) or as fertilizer (human and animal faeces, the inedible portions of plants and ash). Inorganic wastes such as broken pottery and tools were tipped outside the settlement and could be forgotten about.

As settlements grew, waste became more of a problem and the amount of waste produced exceeded the ability of the local environment to assimilate the wastes back into the ecosystem. From this point forward, technology had to be developed to collect and dispose of society's wastes. Archaeologists have identified sewage pipes in the remains of the ancient cities in Mesopotamia and the Indus valley. Similar investigations have shown that in the Cretan capital of Knossos in 3000 BCE, waste was taken to pits, deposited and covered with earth.

The medieval cities of Europe adopted a less-advanced approach than these ancient cultures and allowed householders to leave their waste in the gutters for the rain to wash away. In 1297 a law was passed in England that made householders responsible for keeping the front of their houses free of refuse. In practice this law was largely ignored and waste was either dumped in the streets or burned on open fires. In London a weekly waste collection began in 1354 when 'rakers' were paid to rake waste together in the streets, load it into carts and remove it for disposal outside the city. Other cities used slave labour or prisoners to carry out a similar task.

An interesting system developed in Amsterdam when, in 1473, a commercial organization paid for the right to collect organic waste from the city which was then sold to farmers in rural areas for use as a fertilizer. This practice was adopted in other cities, but eventually the increasing volumes of waste meant that it was difficult to find people who could use all the materials collected, so the cities had to pay the waste collectors. This experience neatly sums up the present-day economics of waste management. Wastes may contain usable materials, but the cost of collecting them and finding markets for the products means that the waste collectors have to be paid for providing this service. You will see echoes of this story when you come to read about waste recycling and composting later on in this block.

The industrial revolution in the 18th and 19th centuries gave rise to massive increases in manufactured goods and, in turn, to massive increases in wastes. Many of these materials were inorganic and could not be used as fertilizers, so disposal to farmland was not an option. The growth of cities and the concentration of populations brought about by the development of factories added to the problem of collecting and disposing of these new wastes.

Cities and towns began to organize waste collection and disposal systems but, as often occurs, there was a long time lag before legislation forced local authorities to deal with their waste. The process of waste regulation began with The Public Health Act of 1848 and was strengthened by the 1875 Public Health Act, which required authorities to collect waste at weekly intervals from households. This Act also required householders to store their waste in a 'movable receptacle' while awaiting collection. It is interesting to note that weekly waste collections were implemented both for convenience and as a measure to control flies. Normally, it takes longer than one week for blowfly eggs to hatch, so any eggs laid in a dustbin would have been removed before they could hatch and cause problems.

Waste recycling and recovery systems also continued to develop during the industrial revolution and the first plant that burned waste while recovering energy was built in Nottingham in 1874. In the following 30 years some 250 of these so-called 'destructors' were built across Britain. These plants eliminated the risk to human health from pathogens in the waste and reduced the amount of residue for final disposal, but they did emit ash, dust, charred paper and gases from their chimneys. Consequently there was much public opposition to incineration. By 1945 most plants had closed and the waste was disposed of in landfill sites, although 34 such plants were still operating in 1991.

The collection of waste for recycling into new materials also developed during the 19th century and the British Paper Company was set up in

1890 to make paper and board from waste paper collected by 'rag and bone men' and organizations such as the Salvation Army. In precursors to today's 'materials recovery facilities' (which we will look at in Chapter 11) salvageable materials were removed from mixed waste. Glass and metals were returned to producers and ashes were used in building materials. As you can imagine, this was not a safe or hygienic working environment and the workers (mainly women and young girls) paid with their health and quality of life to recycle these materials (although the term 'recycling' was probably not used at that time).

So where are we now with waste management? Waste is still collected from our houses at weekly intervals (although in some areas recyclable and non-recyclable wastes are collected on alternate weeks – possibly a step backwards when it comes to blowflies and related nuisances/hazards). Most of the UK's household waste is landfilled, but we still have versions of the materials recovery, compost manufacture and energy recovery processes that our ancestors knew. Indeed, the delegate to the Association of Cleansing Superintendents conference who, in 1907, said that the biggest change in municipal waste collection will be the change from destruction to salvage would still be waiting for this to happen.

On the other hand, we have made great leaps forward in the UK: landfills are regulated and carefully controlled; incinerators operate to tighter emission standards than conventional power stations; and the health concerns of materials recovery facilities are beginning to be addressed.

In the remainder of this block, we will look at the present state of waste management, how technology can help to solve the problems associated with waste, and where we still need to make improvements.

1.3 How much waste does the UK produce today?

Before looking at the individual waste streams in detail it is useful to get an idea of the size of the problem we are dealing with. The Department for Environment, Food and Rural Affairs (Defra) estimates that in 2004 the UK produced about 335 million tonnes of waste a year (Defra 2006). This is broken down by broad category in Figure 3.

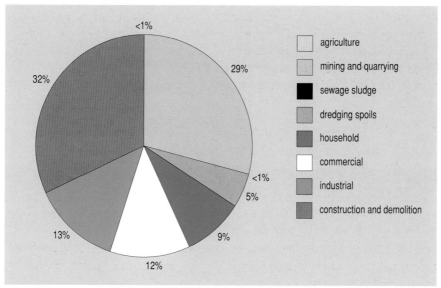

Figure 3   Total UK waste arisings 2004 (source: http://defra.gov.uk/ environment/statistics/waste/kf/wrkf02.htm)

Non-controlled wastes

Mining and quarrying wastes, sewage sludge and dredging spoils account for over a third of the total and have generally been regarded as having a relatively low potential for causing harm to human health or the environment. But note that in Block 3 you considered the potential for aquatic pollution from silage liquor and the restrictions for disposing of sewage sludge on land. Wastes from mines and quarries tend to consist of relatively inert minerals. Sewage sludge has traditionally been spread on agricultural land (although it is becoming more difficult to find suitable land) and dredging spoils can be considered to consist of wet soil.

Controlled wastes

In contrast, the municipal, commercial, construction and demolition, and industrial waste streams contain many materials that inevitably produce environmentally damaging by-products when they undergo the natural degradation processes. Other components are themselves toxic or hazardous to health in other ways. Figure 4 shows the breakdown of this 225 million tonnes of controlled waste by category.

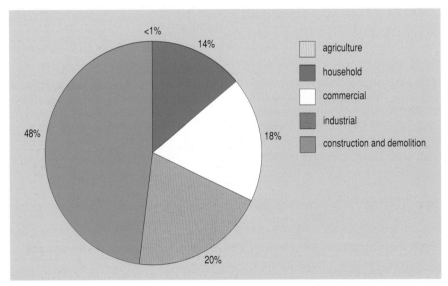

Figure 4   UK controlled waste arisings (source: after Defra (2006))

STUDY NOTE

In the course of your T210 studies you will see many figures relating to wastes. These figures should carry 'health warnings' regarding their accuracy. Until relatively recently, most waste was not weighed at the point of disposal and no reliable statistics were obtained on industrial and commercial wastes. The situation is improving as a result of surveys carried out by Defra and the Environment Agency. But you should still regard all figures relating to waste as estimates (even those quoted in your course materials).

1.4   A few terms and definitions

Like all disciplines, waste management has its own jargon and attaches highly specific meanings to some everyday terms. To help you through this, I have put together a summary of some of the more important terms used to describe wastes in Table 1 below. They are all discussed in detail elsewhere in this block, but the table should give you an idea of what to expect.

Table I   Waste management terms

Term	Meaning	See Chapter/Section
Inert waste	Wastes that pose virtually no environmental or health threat on disposal (e.g. ceramics, rocks, etc.)	4, 6
Municipal solid waste	Household waste and wastes from small businesses collected alongside household waste	3
Household waste	The waste produced in domestic households and gardens	3
Hazardous waste	Waste with the greatest potential for causing harm to the environment or public health (e.g. toxic substances, flammable liquids, asbestos, strong acids and alkalis, etc.)	5
Clinical waste	Wastes generated by healthcare activities (GPs, hospitals, vets, laboratories, etc.). The waste ranges from used sticking plasters to drugs and human organs	6.2
Industrial waste	Waste produced by manufacturing industry (can cover everything from inert to hazardous waste)	4
Commercial waste	Waste produced by commercial businesses (similar to household waste but tends to contain more paper products)	4
Special waste	A technical term formerly used to describe specific hazardous wastes	5
Radioactive waste	Waste that undergoes radioactive decay	16
Biodegradable waste	Waste that can be broken down by microbial action	2.2.1, 8.1, 10, 11.6

1.5   The impact of waste on public health and the environment

Why does waste have the potential to harm human health and the environment? The answer to this may seem obvious. (I have already mentioned blowflies and the impact from the unregulated burning of wastes.) Waste is generally unsightly and unpleasant but here are a few possibly more-serious health impacts from household wastes:

- infection from nappies, hygiene products, animal faeces and contaminated foods;

- injury from glass, food cans, knives, razor blades, etc.;

- poisoning by household cleaning products, garden chemicals, solvents and paints.

When it comes to industrial wastes the potential for harm is even greater. As you will see later in this block these wastes may be corrosive, highly poisonous, flammable, explosive or radioactive.

Household and industrial wastes also have the potential for harming not only the people who generate them, but also those employed in their collection, treatment and disposal.

Wastes management also has the potential for causing environmental pollution at the local, national and global scale by, for example:

- the congestion, noise and air pollution impacts of waste collection;
- the visual, noise, dust and odour impacts of any waste treatment facility;
- the potential for water contamination from landfill;
- gaseous emissions from incineration;
- ozone depletion from the CFCs present in fridges manufactured before 1995;
- the emission of greenhouse gases (methane and carbon dioxide) from landfill sites.

You have already met the effects of ozone depletion and emission of greenhouse gases in Block 1: *The environment, risk and public health*.

The role of wastes management is to ensure that wastes are collected, treated and disposed of while ensuring that the potential risks to human and environmental health are eliminated or minimized. The remainder of this block looks at ways of achieving this.

1.6   Summary

We all produce waste and we all know what waste is, but arriving at a formal definition is not easy. The key factors that define a waste are that the owner of the material wishes to discard it and that it cannot be used by anyone else without being processed in some way. We will be looking at processing methods later in this block.

Waste has been produced since earliest times, but only started to become a problem when humankind gave up its nomadic existence and began to settle in villages and towns. The growth of cities and the industrial revolution exacerbated the problems of wastes and the pollution that they can cause.

The UK produces about 335 million tonnes of wastes a year. About 225 million tonnes, mainly from the industrial, commercial and domestic sectors, have the greatest potential for causing harm to public health and the environment. These wastes are known as 'controlled wastes' and form the bulk of the discussions in this block.

2 WASTE MANAGEMENT REGULATION AND POLICY

For details of waste regulation and legislation, please refer to the Legislation Supplement. The following paragraphs will give you a broad outline of the areas of responsibility and a summary of UK waste policy.

2.1 Policy and regulatory responsibilities

Several organizations are responsible for waste regulation across the UK. The organizations and their roles and responsibilities with respect to waste are as follows:

- The Department for Environment, Food and Rural Affairs (Defra) is responsible for developing and implementing waste policy in England and to a lesser extent in Wales. Defra also represents the UK in developing European waste policies together with representatives from other EU Member States and has the responsibility for implementing EU directives relating to waste for all parts of the UK.

- The Scottish Parliament and the Northern Ireland Assembly develop and implement waste policies relating to Scotland and Northern Ireland respectively.

- In Wales, the Welsh Assembly has its own policy on wastes management.

The Environment Agency is the regulatory body for wastes in England and Wales. The Agency's principal aim is:

> to protect and improve the environment and make a contribution towards the delivery of sustainable development through the integrated management of emissions to air, land and water.

The equivalent bodies in Scotland and Northern Ireland are the Scottish Environment Protection Agency (SEPA) and the Northern Ireland Environment and Heritage Service (NIEHS).

2.2 An outline of policy

Like much environmental pollution control policy, the UK's waste policies are being developed and implemented in parallel with EU-wide policies. In the UK, waste policy builds on the Government's Sustainable Development Strategy 'A better quality of life', and outlines the significant change that will be required if waste management is to become an environmentally sustainable activity.

To achieve this aim, those responsible for managing wastes (chiefly businesses and local authorities) will have to apply the principle of *best practicable environmental option (BPEO)*. BPEO means ensuring that the waste management options selected for a particular site provide the greatest environmental benefit (or cause the least environmental damage) taking account of the environment as a whole (air, land and water). You should note that the term 'practicable' not only applies to the technical issues involved but also the economic ones. Therefore, costs must be considered when determining what represents the BPEO.

The 'waste hierarchy' forms a useful guide to determining the BPEO and options that should be considered. The hierarchy lists the following options in decreasing importance of desirability:

1   reduction of the amount of waste to be managed;

2   reuse of products and materials;

3   recovery of value through materials recycling, composting and energy recovery;

4   disposal of wastes where there is no other solution.

Waste planners should also use the 'proximity principle' in developing waste management solutions. This principle states that wastes should generally be disposed of as close to the point of production as possible. This prevents the export of problems to other regions and countries, and recognizes that waste transport can have a significant environmental impact.

Pollution does not respect national boundaries. Also, countries that allow their companies to reduce costs by adopting lax environmental standards give these companies an unfair advantage when it comes to international trade. For both these reasons waste policies and standards are developed at the European level and all Member States are required to adopt them.

The Legislation Supplement contains a list of relevant European directives, and several of them are referred to in this block. For the present, the main directives that you need to be aware of are the waste framework directive and the directive on the landfill of waste. The landfill directive was passed in June 1999 and incorporated into UK law in the summer of 2002. It is resulting in a major shift in the way we manage all our wastes. Not surprisingly, you will see references to this directive throughout the block and it is summarized in Section 2.2.3.

2.2.1   The national waste strategies

Before reading on, work through the following activity to find out what your national Parliament/Assembly is planning to do with waste in the long term.

> *Find the website of your national organization responsible for waste strategy development (site details are given on the T210 website) and spend a few minutes finding out what it has to say about its strategy for dealing with wastes.*

England

The document 'Waste Strategy for England 2007' was published in May 2007 and sets out the Government's plans to develop more sustainable ways of dealing with waste in England (Defra 2007). This strategy builds on the basis of an earlier strategy published in 2000, but places much more emphasis on the role of waste management in combating climate change. Some of the key points from the strategy are:

- A target to reduce the amount of household waste not re-used, recycled or composted (i.e. used for energy recovery or landfilled) from the 2000 baseline of 22.2 million tonnes to 12.2 million tonnes by 2020.

- Household waste recycling/composting targets of 40% by 2010 and 50% by 2020 (from a level of 27% in 2005-06).

- Municipal waste recovery (recycling, composting and energy recovery) targets of 53% by 2010, 67% by 2015 and 75% by 2020 (from a level of 37% in 2005-06).

- Increasing the amount of non-recyclable municipal waste that is used for energy recovery from the 2007 level of 10% to 25% by 2020. Energy from waste is generally supported and, while not opting for a particular technology, the Government intends to encourage local authorities and businesses to consider the use of anaerobic digestion.

- Development of a system to allow people to opt out of receiving unaddressed direct marketing (or junk mail) and consideration of a move to a system where people have to 'opt in' to receive addressed direct marketing (rather than the current opt-out system).

- The Government will work with the retail industry to end the provision of free single use carrier bags.

- Consideration of amending the Packaging Waste Regulations to achieve a reduction in packaging use.

- An expansion of recycling facilities in public spaces (parks, shopping centres, exhibition centres, etc).

- The Government does not intend to allow local authorities to introduce variable waste charging schemes (also known as 'pay as you throw') but does intend to allow local councils to introduce cost-neutral schemes that will reward householders that participate in recycling schemes at the expense of those who do not.

- There will be a consultation on whether there should be restrictions on the landfilling of biodegradable and/or recyclable materials over and above those due to the landfill directive

Wales

The National Assembly for Wales (NAW) announced its waste strategy in June 2002, which is based on a consultation paper published in July 2001 (NAW, 2001). Among other measures, this strategy calls for:

- a recycling/composting rate of at least 15% by 2003/04 (with at least 5% composting and 5% recycling);

- a recycling/composting rate of at least 25% by 2006/07 (with at least 10% composting and 10% recycling);

- a recycling/composting rate of at least 40% by 2009/10 (with at least 15% composting and 15% recycling).

Scotland

The Scottish waste strategy was developed by SEPA and subsequently adopted by the Scottish Parliament. This strategy set fewer targets than the strategies for England and Wales, but it did set the eleven regional Waste Strategy Areas the task of producing regional waste management plans. These plans have been issued in draft for consultation (SEPA, 2002). Each plan is different, reflecting local circumstances, but most set targets for reducing landfill and for increasing municipal recycling and recovery rates. Scotland also intends to ensure compliance with the landfill directive by issuing tradable permits to each local authority (as described above).

Northern Ireland

The Northern Ireland waste strategy was published in March 2000 (NIEHS, 2000) following a three-year consultation exercise. The strategy sets a number of targets relating to household and municipal waste. These targets are provisional and will be reviewed and possibly put on a statutory basis in 2003. The key targets are:

■ to recover materials or energy from 25% of household waste by 2005 and 40% by 2010;

■ to recycle 15% of household waste by 2005 and 25% by 2010;

■ to reduce the landfilling of biodegradable municipal waste to 75% of the 1995 level by 2010, 50% by 2013 and 35% by 2020;

This implements the EU packaging directive under 'producer responsibility' as outlined in Section 2.2.2.

■ to reduce household waste generation to the 1998 level by 2005 and then reduce it by 1% every three years.

SAQ 2

Make brief comments on the similarities and differences between the waste strategies for England and Northern Ireland.

2.2.2   Producer responsibility

One way of dealing with a product or material when it becomes a waste is to place a responsibility on the original producer to ensure that the product or material is disposed of in an environmentally sensitive manner. This idea of 'producer responsibility' is already being used to increase the recycling of packaging material (see waste strategy targets for England). Packaging manufacturers, the manufacturers of packaged goods and the retail sector have a joint responsibility to ensure that the UK complies with the packaging waste targets. Producer responsibility is being extended to recover scrap vehicles and electrical goods and may be extended to other products/materials in the future.

2.2.3   The landfill directive

The overall aim of the landfill directive (Council of the European Union, 1999) is to prevent, or reduce as far as possible, any negative impacts on human health or the environment due to the landfilling of waste. In particular, it is concerned with preventing pollution of surface and ground waters, pollution of soils and air pollution.

SAQ 3

One of the key pollutants relating to landfills is landfill gas – a mixture of methane and carbon dioxide. Why is methane such a significant pollutant? (It may help you to revisit the section on the carbon cycle in Block 1.)

Under the directive, reducing the impact of landfills is to be achieved by several measures designed to improve their operation and management and to restrict the types of waste that are allowed to be landfilled. The main requirements of the directive are summarized below.

■ Landfills must be classed as being suitable for hazardous, non-hazardous or inert wastes.

■ The amount of biodegradable municipal waste (paper, kitchen and garden waste and natural textiles) going to landfill must be reduced to:

75% of the weight of biodegradable municipal waste produced in 1995 by 2004;

50% of the weight of biodegradable municipal waste produced in 1995 by 2007;

35% of the weight of biodegradable municipal waste produced in 1995 by 2014. Member States that landfilled over 80% of their MSW before implementation of the directive (including the UK) may delay any of these targets by up to four years.

■ The following wastes must be banned from landfill:

liquid waste;

explosive materials, highly-flammable wastes, corrosive or oxidizing wastes;

certain types of chemical waste from research and teaching activities;

infectious wastes from hospitals and other medical and veterinary premises;

whole tyres by 2001 and shredded tyres by 2004.

■ Only waste that has been pre-treated (to reduce its mass, hazardousness or environmental impact) may be landfilled.

■ The co-disposal of hazardous and non-hazardous wastes in the same landfill will not be permitted.

■ All landfill sites must have permits and be operated by technically competent staff and financially sound organizations.

■ The price charged by landfill site operators must reflect the true cost of setting up and operating the site and of providing for site closure and aftercare.

■ Measures must be put in place to verify that all wastes delivered to a landfill are permitted to be deposited at that site and that a register is kept of all wastes deposited.

■ Environmental monitoring must be carried out at all sites.

■ Sites may only be closed after inspection by the regulatory authority, and the site operator is responsible for carrying out monitoring and maintenance for as long as the site is likely to present any environmental hazards (at least 30 years, and probably much longer in the case of sites that take biodegradable wastes).

Many of these requirements (such as permits, monitoring and post-closure responsibilities) are already required in the UK, but other requirements such as the ban on hazardous and non-hazardous waste co-disposal and the reduction in biodegradable waste landfilling will have a major impact on waste management in the UK.

In order to meet the biodegradable MSW diversion requirements, it has been estimated (Burnley et al., 1999) that the UK will need to divert some

15 million tonnes of MSW from landfill by 2020. Achieving these targets could require the construction and operation of up to:

■ 70 composting plants (capacity 20 000 tonne/year per plant);

■ 115 recycling plants (capacity 50 000 tonne/year per plant);

■ 50 incineration plants (capacity 250 000 tonne/year per plant). (You should note that most new incinerators are considerably smaller than this – typically taking 100 000 tonnes per year.)

These figures assume that there is no growth in MSW production. If the recent estimated growth rate of about 3% per year continues, the figures could rise to:

■ 130 composting plants;

■ 210 recycling plants;

■ 145 incinerators.

SAQ 4

In Block 0: *Mathematics and statistics* you looked at compound interest. The same principles also relate to the growth in waste production. If the UK produced 30 million tonnes of MSW in 2000 how much waste will be produced in 2020 assuming annual growth rates of 1% and 3%?

The formula for compound interest is given by

$$A = P\left(1 + \frac{x}{100}\right)^t$$

where

A is the total amount after a time of t years

P is the principal or initial amount

x is the growth rate in %

t is the time period we are considering.

You will have found from SAQ 4 that for a 3% growth rate there is an 80% increase in the amount of waste produced over the 20-year period. This means that, unless waste growth is curbed, the waste industry and local authorities will have to run very fast to keep still.

2.3   Summary

The UK's policy for managing wastes is built on the principles of the Sustainable Development Strategy. It aims to make waste management more sustainable by adopting these principles through the application of 'best practicable environmental option' (BPEO), the waste management hierarchy and the proximity principle. These measures reflect developments at the EU level.

The four constituent parts of the UK have produced their own strategies for managing wastes. All four documents set targets for reductions in the amounts of waste produced and increased recovery of materials and energy from the wastes that are generated.

The biggest policy development in recent years is the EU landfill directive, which calls for higher standards of landfills, bans the landfilling of certain wastes and restricts the landfilling of biodegradable municipal solid waste. One of the main impacts of this directive will be a vast increase in the amount of municipal waste that is recycled or used for energy production.

3 HOUSEHOLD AND MUNICIPAL SOLID WASTES

3.1 What is household and municipal waste?

In simple terms, household waste is the waste that we put out in our dustbins for collection by the local authority or its contractors. However, there are many other materials that also come under the definition of household waste. These are shown in Table 2.

Table 2 Components of household waste

Household waste (collected free of charge)	Household waste (may be charged for collection)
'dustbin' waste	bulky or heavy household items
civic amenity site waste	garden waste
waste from places of worship	waste from local authority public parks and gardens
household recyclable waste	household clinical waste
waste from private garages	campsite waste
street sweepings and street litter	waste from charities
	waste from hostels, and university and hospital halls of residence
	separately collected hazardous household wastes (dead pets, asbestos, oil/grease)
	waste from prisons
	waste from public halls
	waste from royal palaces
	flytipped wastes

Another term that I have already used is 'municipal solid waste' or MSW. The precise meaning of the phrase varies from user to user and from country to country, but a useful working definition that is widely used in the UK is:

> household waste and non-household waste with a similar composition that is collected by, or on behalf of, a local authority.

Under this definition the parts of MSW that are not household waste consist mainly of waste produced by small offices, shops and businesses (if it is collected by a local authority or its contractors). You should note that many other European countries take a much wider view of MSW and include all commercial wastes and industrial wastes that have a similar composition to household waste.

3.2 Quantities of household and municipal waste

I have commented on the problems of producing reliable estimates of our wastes and, until the mid-1990s, there was very little reliable information on the amount of household and municipal waste produced in the UK. The reason for this is simple; there was no need for the information.

Waste was collected by the local authority and generally disposed of in local authority-owned and operated landfill sites. As long as the authority had a reasonable estimate of the volume remaining in its landfill sites, it didn't need any more information.

Since that time, the situation has changed. Waste disposal facilities now tend to be owned and operated by the private sector and local authorities are charged by the tonne for waste that is taken away. Contracts for waste collection are let by competitive tender where tonnages are also important. In addition, HM Revenue and Customs collect *landfill tax* on the basis of tonnage landfilled and Defra requires all local authorities in England and Wales to submit returns of municipal waste generation, recovery and disposal. This information is used by the Government to assist in policy-making and to monitor progress towards recycling and recovery targets.

The estimates for UK MSW production for the year 2005/06 are shown in Table 3. The way this waste is managed in England is summarized in Table 4. This table shows an increase in materials recycling and energy recovery over the years, but there is still some way to go to reach the targets set out in the national waste strategies discussed in Chapter 2. Wales, Scotland and Northern Ireland recycle 22%, 19% and 22% of their MSW respectively, and Scotland sends around 2% to incineration with energy recovery.

Table 3   Quantities of municipal solid waste in the UK (million tonnes)

	England 2005/06	Scotland 2004/05	Wales 2004/05	Northern Ireland 2005/06	Total
Household-collected waste	14.6	2.27	1.0	0.71	18.58
Civic amenity (CA) waste	2.7	a	0.22	a	
'kerbside' recycling collections	6.8	0.52	0.29	0.23	7.84
Bulky waste collections, clinical waste collections from households, litter and street sweepings	1.3	a	0.08	a	
Total household waste	*25.4*	*2.8*	*1.59*	*0.94*	*30.73*
Non-household MSW	2.3	0.58	0.21		
Non-household recycling	1.0	0.13	0.13		
Total non-household MSW	*3.3*	*0.71*	*0.34*	*0.12*	*4.47*
Total MSW	**28.7**	**3.5**	**1.93**	**1.06**	**35.19**

a Included in household-collected.

Source: adapted from Defra (2006), National Assembly for Wales (2006), Environment and Heritage Service (2006), and SEPA (2006).

Research by AEA Technology (Brown *et al.*, 1999) suggests that UK MSW production rose steadily from about 8 million tonnes in 1945 to about 14 million tonnes in 1979. No data are available from 1980 until the mid-1990s, but the recent figures reported above indicate that MSW production has more than doubled over the two decades leading to 2000. However, there is now some evidence to suggest that over the past few years the growth in MSW has slowed down or even halted.

Table 4 Percentage MSW disposal in England

	Landfill	Percentage treated by	
		Incineration with energy recovery	Recycling/ composting
1997/98	85	6	8
1998/99	82	8	10
1999/2000	80	8	11
2000/01	79	9	12
2003/04	72	9	19
2004/05	67	9	23
2005/06	62	10	27

Source: Defra (2006).

SAQ 5

According to AEA Technology's figures what was the mean annual growth rate of MSW over the period 1945 to 1979?

This increase in MSW is partly due to increases in the size of the population and average levels of prosperity, but also other factors such as the increasing use of pre-packaged meals and the decline in families eating together. One other very important factor is the increasing number of households in the UK and the fall in the number of people per household (see Figure 5). However, the amount of waste produced is not directly proportional to the number of people living in the house. For example, my four-person household produces almost the same amount of garden waste as my next door neighbours' two-person household. Similarly, both households receive the same number of free papers and amounts of junk mail.

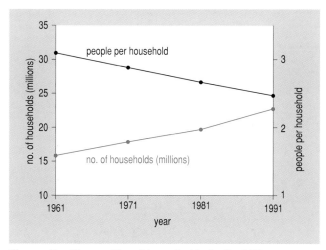

Figure 5 The profile of households in the UK

There are several factors contributing to the increase in the number of households:

■ people are living longer and remaining in their own homes for longer;

■ divorce and the subsequent setting up of two households is increasing;

■ ownership of second homes is more common than in the past.

3.3 Composition of household and municipal waste

The composition of our household waste reflects our lifestyles in many ways. For example, on a basic level we can safely say that:

■ households with young children are the main producers of disposable nappies;

■ households with pets generate large quantities of food cans and, in the case of households with cats, used cat litter;

■ people who eat many ready-prepared meals throw away higher than average amounts of foil containers and lower than average amounts of vegetable peelings and meat trimmings;

■ people who live in medium- and high-rise flats tend not to generate garden waste.

However, the waste collection system supplied by the local authority also influences the amount and type of material that we throw away. For example:

■ people supplied with large wheeled bins tend to throw away more garden waste and DIY waste than people whose waste is collected in plastic sacks;

■ people supplied with a recycling box that is emptied along with their other waste container tend to recycle more than people living in areas where they have to take their waste to recycling facilities;

■ households with easy access to public waste disposal sites (civic amenity sites) tend to dispose of less DIY and garden waste in their dustbins.

In addition to these local differences, patterns emerge over time. For example, the introduction of smoke control legislation in the 1950s and 1960s led to a large reduction in the amounts of ash in household waste. Similarly, the introduction of plastics led to completely new materials appearing in our waste from the 1960s. Some of these trends can be seen in Figure 6.

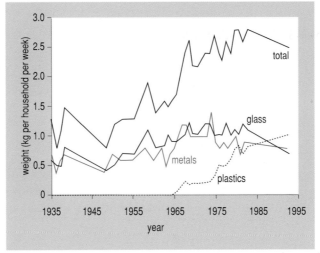

Figure 6 Trends in household waste composition (source: Bridgwater, 1986; Atkinson and New, 1993)

The composition of municipal waste has been investigated in several surveys over the years. The most recent and comprehensive survey was undertaken for the National Assembly for Wales and the results are summarised in Tables 5 and 6.

Table 5 Household waste composition

Waste category	Percentage composition	
	Household-collected waste	CA waste
Paper and card	23.60	9.29
Plastic film (carrier bags, food wrapping)	4.01	0.73
Dense plastic (bottles, packaging)	6.14	2.81
Textiles	5.24	2.68
Wood, carpets and furniture	1.92	23.30
Other miscellaneous combustible items (nappies, wood, leather)	5.70	3.13
Construction and demolition waste (DIY projects)	1.64	17.00
Other miscellaneous non-combustible materials (ceramics)	1.13	1.50
Glass (bottles, jars, flat glass)	7.25	2.78
Kitchen waste (peelings, raw and cooked food)	25.00	2.65
Garden waste	8.32	18.00
Ferrous metal (food and drink cans, etc.)	3.60	6.05
Non-ferrous metal (foil, cans, etc.)	1.04	0.94
Waste electrical and electronic equipment[a]	1.54	6.76
Potentially hazardous material (household chemicals, clinical waste, oil and lead/acid batteries)	0.62	1.46
Fines (materials less than 10 mm in size that cannot be classified easily)	4.55	0.82

[a] Includes white goods and large electronic goods.

Source: Burnley et al. (2007).

Table 6 Non-household MSW composition

Waste category	Percentage composition
Paper and card	41.2
Plastic film (carrier bags, food wrapping)	4.4
Dense plastic (bottles, packaging)	5.5
Textiles	1.6
Wood, carpets and furniture	2.2
Other miscellaneous combustible items (nappies, wood, leather)	4.1
Construction and demolition waste (DIY projects)	0.5

Waste category	Percentage composition
Other miscellaneous non-combustible materials (ceramics)	1.4
Glass (bottles, jars, flat glass)	4.1
Kitchen waste (peelings, raw and cooked food)	23.2
Garden waste	3.0
Ferrous metal (food and drink cans etc)	4.1
Non-ferrous metal (foil, cans etc)	0.9
Waste electrical and electronic equipment	0.9
Potentially hazardous material (household chemicals, clinical waste, oil and lead/acid batteries)	0.8
Fines (materials less than 10 mm in size that cannot be classified easily)	1.4

Source: Burnley et al. (2007).

SAQ 6

Assume that household waste consists of 75% household-collected waste and 25% material having a similar composition to civic amenity (CA) waste. Use the information in Tables 5 and 6 to complete the table below showing the overall composition of household waste.

Note that you will use this table in some of the following SAQs.

Overall composition of household waste

Waste category	Composition (%)
Paper and card	20
Plastic film	3.2
Dense plastic	5.3
Textiles	4.6
Wood, carpets and furniture	7.3
Other miscellaneous combustible items	5.1
Construction and demolition waste	5.5
Other miscellaneous non-combustible materials	1.2
Glass	6.1
Kitchen waste	19.4
Garden waste	10.7
Ferrous metal	4.2
Non-ferrous metal	1.0
Waste electrical and electronic equipment	2.8
Potentially hazardous material	0.8
Fines	3.6

3.4 Household waste collection and disposal responsibilities

In England, responsibility for collecting and disposing of household waste is divided between the district and county councils. The district councils have the role of 'waste collection authorities' (WCAs) and are responsible for the weekly household waste collection and for the collection of commercial wastes if requested. These services are carried out by the council's own workforce or by contractors acting on behalf of the council.

Waste disposal is the responsibility of the waste disposal authority (WDA) of the county council. The WDA has to place and manage contracts for the disposal of the wastes collected by the WCAs and the WDA-operated civic amenity sites. One result of the 1990 Environmental Protection Act was to privatize waste disposal, so most waste disposal facilities (landfill sites, incinerators, recycling plants) tend to be privately owned.

The 'unitary authorities' combine the roles of county and district authorities in one body and are responsible for both waste collection and disposal.

In Wales and Scotland, all the local authorities are unitary authorities so they have the responsibility for both waste collection and disposal functions in the same way as English unitary authorities.

In Northern Ireland, responsibility for waste collection and disposal rests with the district councils. However, the Northern Ireland waste strategy suggests that groups of councils should be encouraged to work together to create more cost-effective collection and disposal systems.

3.5 Summary

Household waste consists of the materials we put into our dustbins each week, and also the wastes we take to civic amenity sites and recycling centres or put out for collection by house-to-house recycling schemes. Other wastes, such as street sweepings and litter, are also classed as household waste.

Municipal waste covers household waste plus any industrial or commercial waste collected alongside household waste (for example, wastes from corner shops and small offices).

Reliable data on the amounts of household and municipal waste produced were not available until the mid-1990s and there is still some uncertainty about current figures, but it does appear that household waste generation is increasing. Best estimates suggest that the UK produced 33 million tonnes of municipal waste in the year 1999/2000 and 30 million tonnes of this was household waste. There is even less certainty over the composition of household and municipal waste.

Most municipal waste is disposed of by landfilling. In the year 2004/05 England sent around two thirds or 19.2 million tonnes to landfill, 23% (6.6 million tonnes) to recycling or composting and 9% (2.6 million tonnes) for energy recovery.

4   COMMERCIAL AND INDUSTRIAL WASTES

Over the period October 1998 to April 1999, the Environment Agency undertook a survey of industrial and commercial waste production in England and Wales (Environment Agency, 2002). This was the biggest national waste survey ever undertaken and involved telephone calls and visits to 20 000 premises ranging from self-employed one-person businesses to large petro-chemical plants. The Environment Agency has published the results of the survey and most of the information provided in this chapter is based on this work.

4.1   Quantities of industrial and commercial wastes

The Agency survey estimated that England and Wales produced about 30.3 million tonnes of commercial waste and 37.6 million tonnes of industrial wastes in 2002/03. These figures are for wastes currently classed as controlled wastes and so exclude wastes from mining and quarrying, etc. Wastes produced by the construction and demolition sector, which are discussed in Chapter 6, are also excluded from these data.

The Scottish Environment Protection Agency (SEPA) estimates that Scotland produced 2.6 million tonnes of industrial waste (excluding construction and demolition) and 6.4 million tonnes of commercial waste in 2004. The Environment Agency also estimated the amounts produced in Wales in 2002/03 at 1.03 million tonnes of commercial and 4.24 million tonnes of industrial waste.

The estimated combined commercial and industrial waste arisings for Northern Ireland is 700 000 tonnes per year. Breakdowns of the figures for England and Wales by sector are shown in Tables 7 and 8.

Table 7   Commercial waste production (England and Wales)

Sector	Annual waste production (million tonnes)
Retail and wholesale	12.75
Public sector	3.33
Other services	14.24
Total	30.32

Source: Environment Agency (2006).

Table 8   Industrial waste production (England and Wales)

Sector	Annual waste production (million tonnes)
Food, drink and tobacco	7.23
Textiles, wood, paper and publishing	6.70
Chemical and non-metallic minerals	7.53
Metal manufacture	4.82
Machinery and equipment (other manufacturing)	5.13
Power and utilities	6.18
Total	37.59

Source: Environment Agency (2006).

4.2   Composition of industrial and commercial wastes

The amount of information on the composition of commercial and industrial waste varies greatly between sectors. In general, the activities that produce large volumes of particular waste streams tend to have the most reliable data on both the amounts generated and their physical and chemical compositions. Such waste streams contain well-characterized and homogeneous materials, which achieve high recycling rates.

The power generation industry in the UK produced 5.5 million tonnes of ash in 1999, and the iron and steel industry produces 5.5 million tonnes of slag each year. Over 50% of the power station ash and 80% of the steelmaking slag is recycled by the construction industry. Similarly, the paper industry produces around 2.1 million tonnes of waste sludge a year, and 40% of papermaking sludge is recycled by spreading it on agricultural land.

SAQ 7

The power generation industry burned 46 million tonnes of coal in 2000. If coal has an average ash content of 8% and 50% of the ash is sent for recycling how much money is saved by the power generation industry each year. (Assume that the disposal charge for the ash used as landfill is £12 per tonne.)

Conversely, much industrial and commercial waste is known as 'general' industrial or commercial waste. This tends to be the materials deposited in skips and bins for collection and disposal. Like household wastes, this waste can contain many different materials and, once mixed, has a relatively low recycling potential. Very little research has been carried out on its composition, but in general terms it can be considered to be similar to municipal waste, but with larger amounts of paper, plastics and metals, and less kitchen and garden waste.

Table 9 gives a summary of the information obtained during the Environment Agency's survey in 1999.

Table 9   Industrial and commercial waste composition

Waste type	Estimated annual production (million tonnes)
Inert and small-scale in-house construction	2
Paper and card	7
Food	3
Other general and biodegradable waste	9
Metals and scrap equipment	6
Contaminated material and healthcare waste	5
Mineral waste and residues	6
Chemicals	4
General commercial	23
General industrial	13
Total	78

Source: Defra (2000).

4.3   Management of industrial and commercial wastes

The management of the UK's 68 million tonnes of industrial and commercial waste is almost all carried out by the private sector. You will recall from Table 3 that only 4.5 million tonnes of commercial or industrial waste is handled alongside household waste as part of the municipal waste stream.

The management of industrial and commercial wastes has always been driven by ways to find the lowest cost solutions. One effect of the landfill tax has been to reinforce this. Consequently, the business sector will tend to find and implement beneficial uses for its wastes where this can be done reliably and at a lower cost than landfill disposal. This fact is reflected in Table 10, which shows how industrial and commercial wastes are managed.

Table 10   Industrial and commercial waste management in England

Waste type	Percentage recovered		Percentage disposed	
	Recycled	Other	Direct to landfill	Other
Chemicals	20	7	31	41
Metallic	91	0	4	5
Non-metallic	85	1	8	6
Discarded equipment	61	0	14	26
Animal and plant residues	49	11	11	29
Mixed wastes	9	0	77	14
Sludges	25	26	9	41
Mineral wastes	49	0	47	4
Total	42	2	41	15

Source: Environment Agency (2006).

Table 10 shows that industrial and commercial wastes have an overall recycling rate of 42% or 28.7 million tonnes. In comparison we have seen that the municipal recycling rate in England stands at 23% or 6.8 million tonnes.

SAQ 8

Why are commercial and industrial waste recycling rates so much higher than for municipal waste?

4.4   Summary

Commercial and industrial wastes are produced by manufacturing industry, the wholesale and retail sectors, and the catering, educational and administration sectors.

We have less information about the quantities and composition of these wastes than municipal wastes, but estimates for England from 2002/03 suggest that it produces 30 million tonnes of commercial and 38 million tonnes of industrial waste a year (excluding construction and demolition waste and non-controlled wastes). Scotland produces about 2.6 million tonnes and 6.4 million tonnes of industrial and commercial waste respectively. Wales generated 1.03 million tonnes of commercial and 4.24 million tonnes of industrial waste whilst Northern Ireland produced a combined total of around 700 000 tonnes.

The management of these wastes is almost entirely in the private sector, with about 44% of England's waste recovered (mainly by recycling) and 56% landfilled.

5   HAZARDOUS WASTES

> **STUDY NOTE**
>
> Following changes to hazardous waste legislation at the European level, the UK is developing new national regulations. This chapter is based on the Environmental Agency's draft consultation document issued in September 2002. Please see the Legislation Guide for recent developments.

SAQ 9

Before starting to read this chapter, take a few moments to think about the sort of wastes that you would describe as hazardous. Then make a list of materials that you would put in this category and add a few words to explain why they are hazardous.

5.1   Definitions and classification

I am sure that you will have come up with a reasonable list of materials and sensible criteria for selection. But did you have any difficulties? For example, would the amount of material present or the concentration of the hazardous component influence your decision? Perhaps you found a waste that would be hazardous in some circumstances but not in others? Did you have any difficulties in deciding which hazards to consider?

Regulators have had to face problems such as these for many years. You may have already deduced that virtually any waste can be hazardous in particular circumstances. However, it is generally recognized that certain wastes, by virtue of their toxicity, flammability, corrosiveness or otherwise dangerous nature, require special care in handling and disposal.

The following is a useful working definition of hazardous waste:

> **hazardous wastes are wastes that have a serious potential for harming living organisms and the environment.**

The Environment Agency has published detailed guidance on how to assess and classify hazardous wastes. However, in general terms a hazardous waste is any waste included in the European Waste Catalogue and marked with an asterisk.

Some of these marked wastes are considered to be hazardous regardless of their composition. Others are only to be classed as hazardous if their composition means that they exhibit one or more of the properties listed in the box below.

HAZARDOUS PROPERTIES

Explosive – Substances that may explode under the action of a flame or are more sensitive to shock or friction than dinitrobenzene

Oxidizing – Substances that exhibit highly exothermic reactions in contact with other substances (particularly flammable substances)

Highly flammable – Substances that:

■ have a flash point below 21 °C

■ may ignite in contact with air at ambient temperature without any source of ignition

■ readily ignite in the presence of an ignition source and continue to burn when the source is removed

■ are flammable gases

■ release dangerous quantities of flammable gases in contact with water or damp air

Flammable – Liquids having a flash point between 21 °C and 55 °C

Irritant – Non-corrosive substances that, through prolonged or repeated contact, cause inflammation of the skin or mucous membranes

Harmful – Substances that, if inhaled, ingested or allowed to penetrate the skin, may involve limited health risks

Toxic – Substances that, if inhaled, ingested or allowed to penetrate the skin, may involve serious, acute or chronic health risks or even death

Carcinogenic – Substances that, if inhaled, ingested or allowed to penetrate the skin, may induce cancer or increase its incidence

Corrosive – Substances that may destroy living tissue on contact

Infectious – Substances containing viable micro-organisms or their toxins which are known or reliably believed to cause disease in humans of other living organisms

Toxic for reproduction – Substances that, if inhaled, ingested or allowed to penetrate the skin, may induce non-hereditary adverse effects in the progeny or reproductive functions, or increase their incidence

Mutagenic – Substances that, if inhaled, ingested or allowed to penetrate the skin, may induce hereditary genetic defects or increase their incidence

Ecotoxic – Substances that may present immediate or delayed risk to one or more sectors of the environment

Any substances that release toxic gases in contact with water, air or acids

Any substances capable of generating another substance that has any of the listed properties after disposal (for example, producing a leachate that is irritant, toxic, etc.)

An exothermic reaction is one that releases heat (refer to Block 0: *Chemistry* for further details).

5.2   What does hazardous waste classification mean?

If a waste is classed as a hazardous waste this has important implications for the producer of the waste and the way it is handled, transported and finally disposed of.

Completion of consignment note

The producer of a hazardous waste completes a 'consignment note' which gives details of the waste and where it is to be treated. Note that electronic consignment notes may be introduced in the future.

Transport of the waste

When the waste is collected for transport, the carrier (who must be licensed to carry hazardous waste) signs the consignment note to confirm that they have collected the material listed. The producer also signs to confirm that the waste described has been transferred to a licensed carrier.

Arrival at the treatment/disposal facility

On arrival at the treatment or disposal facility the organization receiving the waste completes the final part of the form to certify that the waste described on the form has been received from the specified carrier.

The receiver of the waste then sends a copy of the completed forms to the Environment Agency. This system may sound bureaucratic, but it ensures that a comprehensive audit trail is kept. This helps to prevent the illegal dumping of hazardous wastes by unscrupulous carriers or receivers of the waste. Also, the completed forms help the Environment Agency to build up a picture of hazardous waste generation and disposal by industrial sector and geographical region. This assists the Government in its waste planning work.

5.3   Sources and disposal of hazardous wastes

As I have said several times already, there is little information available on the production, composition or disposal of hazardous waste. However, the Environment Agency has done much to remedy this for England and Wales in recent years.

In summary the UK produced about 4.8 million tonnes of hazardous waste in 2003. About 1 million tonnes comprises construction and demolition waste (usually due to the presence of asbestos). Oil and oil/water mixtures accounted for a further 900 000 tonnes. The other main producers of hazardous waste are the organic chemical industry, waste and water treatment processes and thermal processes (such as incineration).

The current main disposal routes for hazardous wastes are shown in Table 11. Most of the headings in this table are self-explanatory, but you should note that the term 'treatment' covers any physical, chemical or biological processes that either reduce the quantity of the waste or its hazardous nature. (For example, treatment of acidic or alkaline wastes with lime or acids respectively, the use of oxidizing agents to break down chemical wastes and the physical separation of oil from water are commonly used processes.) Details of the main processes for treating hazardous wastes are discussed in Chapter 15.

Generally, solvent combustion processes account for the bulk of energy-recovery-based hazardous waste disposal methods, while organic chemical waste disposal accounts for 70% of the incineration without energy recovery. Not surprisingly, construction and demolition waste is the largest category of waste sent to landfill and most of the recycled hazardous waste consists of packaging materials, filter materials and oily wastes. Oil and oil/water mixtures also account for the largest category of hazardous waste sent for treatment.

Table 11   Hazardous waste treatment in the UK (2003)

Process	Tonnage	%
Incineration with energy recovery	120 500	2.5
Incineration without energy recovery	89 400	1.9
Landfill	1 800 900	37.7
Long term storage	5 400	0.1
Recycling/reuse	920 200	19.3
Transfer	501 100	10.5
Treatment	1 334 700	28.0
Total	4 772 300	

SAQ 10

The implementation of the landfill directive in 2002 is changing the way we manage hazardous wastes in the UK. Read Chapter 2 again and say what changes you would expect and why.

5.4   Summary

Certain wastes have a particular potential for causing harm to humans or the environment during their collection, transport and disposal. Such wastes are known as 'hazardous wastes' (previously known as special wastes).

The UK produces about 4.8 million tonnes of hazardous waste a year. This is mainly construction and demolition waste containing asbestos, waste oils and wastes produced by the chemicals industry.

Slightly under 40% is landfilled and 28% is processed to reduce its volume or hazardous nature. Around one fifth is recycled and 2.5% incinerated with energy recovery.

6 OTHER WASTE STREAMS

6.1 Construction and demolition wastes

The construction and demolition (C&D) industries produce significant amounts of waste (excavated soils, bricks, stones, concrete and road materials, etc.). Much of this material can be reused with little or no processing (apart from sorting), particularly in foundations and similar structures. C&D wastes are also reused in landfill sites to provide basic engineering materials for use in roadways and in constructing the cells that the waste is deposited in.

C&D waste is substantially inert and presents little environmental risk when landfilled. However, reuse has many environmental benefits, not least the reduced demand for natural aggregates and reductions in the environmental emissions involved in transporting natural aggregates from the point of extraction (often a rural area) to the point of use (often an urban area).

Defra estimates that England produces around 91 million tonnes of construction and demolition waste a year. Surveys carried out on behalf of the devolved administrations estimate that Scotland produces around 7.3 million tonnes a year and Wales and Northern Ireland produce about 5 million tonnes each. However, these results are based on surveys of industrial and waste management companies and have wide margins of error.

The composition of C&D waste is typically as follows:

- 46% hard demolition waste such as concrete and bricks;

- 33% soil (including some stones and rocks);

- 21% mixed hard materials, soils and small amounts of other inert materials.

In England 50% of construction and demolition waste is reused or recycled (generally as aggregates after screening and/or crushing). 18% is disposed of in landfills, but some of this is used in landfill engineering displacing virgin materials. A further 18% is disposed of at 'exempt sites'. Exempt sites are those that are registered with the national regulator but not 'licensed' by the regulator – such sites are subject to rules on the type and quantities of waste that can be handled, but otherwise are not as tightly controlled as licensed sites. The remaining 14% is used to restore quarries. Figure 7 shows a breakdown of disposal method for each category for England.

SAQ 11

List some of the environmental impacts that can be avoided by reusing demolition wastes as aggregate rather than quarrying and using new materials.

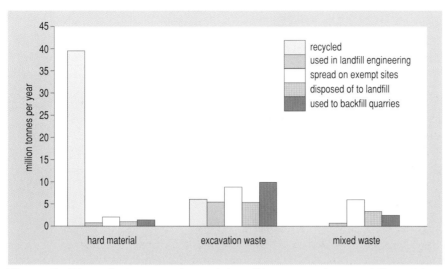

Figure 7   Disposal of construction and demolition wastes (source: Office of the Deputy Prime Minister, 2004)

6.2   Healthcare waste

SAQ 12

Before reading this section and concerning yourself with formal definitions, make a list of all the types of establishment that you would expect to produce healthcare waste.

You will have come up with a wide range of establishments depending on how you have chosen to define the term 'healthcare waste'. Now read the following material and see if there were any wastes you neglected or wastes that you put into this classification which official definitions treat differently.

There are many definitions of clinical waste or healthcare waste, but in the UK clinical waste is defined as:

■   any waste that consists wholly or partly of:

human and animal tissues

blood or other bodily fluids

excretions

drugs or other pharmaceutical products

swabs or dressings

syringes, needles or other sharp implements;

which unless rendered safe may prove hazardous to any person coming into contact with it;

■   any other waste that may cause infection to anyone coming into contact with it that is produced in the following establishments:

medical, nursing, dental, veterinary and pharmaceutical practices

investigation, care, teaching and research

collection of blood for transfusions.

From this definition, we can see that clinical waste is produced in a large number of establishments and, increasingly, in the home.

Clinical wastes have been sub-classified according to the risk of causing infection or other harm to people who come into contact with them. This classification is summarized in Table 12.

Table 12   Clinical waste classification

Group A	Human and animal tissues and blood Soiled surgical dressings and swabs Other wastes from treating infectious diseases not included in Groups B to E
Group B	Syringes and other contaminated sharp items
Group C	Microbiological cultures from pathology and research departments
Group D	Drugs and other pharmaceutical products
Group E	Items used for the disposal of urine and faeces (bedpans, incontinence pads, female hygiene items, etc.)

Detailed information on clinical waste is not available, but it is estimated that UK NHS Trusts produce 193 000 tonnes of clinical waste each year. Other sources are believed to generate between 100 000 and 200 000 tonnes per year.

There are several ways of disposing of clinical waste, often involving a pre-treatment stage to eliminate or reduce the risk of infection. The main pre-treatment methods are heat treatment and chemical treatment. After pre-treatment, landfill is the main disposal route for these wastes.

Wastes that are particularly hazardous or not amenable to pre-treatment are usually incinerated in one of 37 clinical waste incinerators presently operated by private-sector waste companies. These incinerators are regulated under integrated pollution prevention and control (IPPC) (which is covered in the Legislation Supplement) and are required to meet specific operating conditions in terms of furnace temperature and exhaust gas cleaning.

Some clinical wastes in Group E can be macerated and discharged to the sewerage system provided that the hospital has received an authorization to do so from the local water and sewerage company.

6.3   Agricultural wastes

You will recall from Chapter 1 that some classes of agricultural waste have recently been classified as controlled waste. This means that the wastes have to be collected and treated/disposed of at regulated facilities. Former practices such as burning plastics on bonfires and burying chemicals on the farm are no longer legal.

The majority of agricultural wastes consist of organic materials such as crop residues, manures, slurry and silage effluent. Defra estimates that waste from housed livestock alone accounts for some 80 million tonnes per year. The best way of managing these wastes is to apply them to the land in a controlled manner so that they provide organic matter and plant nutrients – reducing the need for fertilizer addition. When managed in this way, the material will not be classed as waste and will not be regulated as such.

After organic materials, the most significant farm wastes are plastic film packaging and sheep dip. Farm film wastes are bulky and often contaminated with soil or chemicals and are therefore expensive to dispose of. The Government is considering schemes for the collection of farm films, including the possibility of introducing a system of producer responsibility (see Section 2.2.2).

Sheep dips are classed as a 'hazardous waste' and must be disposed of according to the appropriate regulations (see Chapter 5). Farms also produce other hazardous wastes including agrochemical packaging, waste oils, batteries and asbestos from old farm buildings. These wastes also need to be disposed of in compliance with the regulations.

6.4   Summary

The construction and demolition, healthcare and agricultural industries all produce significant amounts of wastes.

Based on information for England, about 50% of the UK's 109 million tonnes per year of C&D waste is reused as aggregate, 32% is landfilled and 18% is deposited at exempt sites.

Healthcare waste is generated in many types of establishment and carries the particular hazards of infection. Disposal of this material often involves treatment (by heat or chemical means) to reduce the risk of infection, followed by landfill. Particularly hazardous healthcare wastes are incinerated. Wastes associated with the disposal of urine and faeces can sometimes be macerated and disposed of to the sewers.

Most agricultural waste is animal waste and can be spread on land with beneficial effects. However, farms also produce contaminated plastic films and waste agrochemicals such as sheep dip. Farms also produce hazardous wastes in the form of asbestos, oils, chemical packaging and waste chemicals.

7   A SHORT PAUSE FOR REFLECTION

At this point I feel that it is a good time to take a few moments to summarize what you should have learned at this stage in the block, what you will be covering in the coming sections and how the two fit together.

You should now be familiar with the quantities and types of wastes produced in the UK. In particular:

■   household and municipal solid wastes;

■   industrial and commercial wastes;

■   hazardous wastes;

■   healthcare, agricultural and construction/demolition wastes.

You should also be aware of how these wastes are managed at present.

The way we manage our wastes, and to a lesser extent the amount of waste we produce, is dictated by international and national policies. You should be aware of these policies as stated in the four national waste strategies and in the landfill directive.

In brief, these policies are all designed to ensure that waste is managed in such a way as to eliminate or, failing that, to minimize any adverse effects on human health and on the wider environment. Therefore all waste management solutions should be based on the principle of 'best practicable environmental option' or BPEO. BPEO must be evaluated on a case-by-case basis, but the waste management hierarchy provides a guide to this:

1   reduction

2   reuse

3   recovery

4   disposal.

In the following chapters I am going to discuss the various waste management options in turn. At first sight it may appear odd that I begin at the bottom of the waste management hierarchy with landfill and then work my way up, ending with waste reduction. However, in order to understand why it is environmentally desirable to move waste management further up the hierarchy it is important to understand the potential for environmental pollution and loss of materials and energy associated with the lower options.

You may also wonder why so much of the emphasis in the following sections is on municipal waste when this material only accounts for about 15% of controlled wastes in the UK. Part of the reason for this is due to policy and legislative drivers. The main impact of the landfill directive is related to the need to divert municipal waste from landfill and the national recycling and recovery targets all apply to municipal or household wastes. Municipal waste also has many unique problems:

■   it is very diffuse, being generated in some 25 million households over an area of $244\,000\ \text{km}^2$;

■   it contains a much wider range of materials than any given industrial waste stream;

■   the producers do not have direct legal responsibility for its safe disposal; and

■   the producers do not pay for waste collection and disposal directly.

Another reason for concentrating on household waste is that, as householders, we can all individually do something about the size and composition of this stream and we can even influence the way it is managed.

Once you have worked through these chapters you will also begin to understand the advantages and limitations of each option and how they can be combined to produce a solution that brings us towards BPEO.

Once you have achieved a sound understanding of the technologies available for dealing with wastes, we look at three waste streams with particular problems. In dealing with these wastes we need to bring in elements of all the methods and technologies that we have studied. These wastes are:

- hazardous wastes;

- radioactive wastes;

- contaminated land.

8   LANDFILL

Landfill is probably the oldest method of waste management. There are biblical references to the practice and the word 'hell' (traditionally taken to mean a place of corruption, foul gases and fires) comes from the valley of Gehenna where Jerusalem's waste was disposed of in Old Testament times.

At its crudest, landfill consists of tipping waste into a hole in the ground, covering it with soil and forgetting about it. Until the 1970s this is more or less how many landfills were operated in the UK and many developing countries still carry out landfilling in this way. Since 1970, landfill in the UK has become a tightly regulated process with restrictions on where sites can be located and mandatory high operational standards and levels of environmental control. You have already considered the landfill directive in Chapter 2 and will recall from this that the period 2000–2020 will see many more changes in the way landfills are operated throughout Europe.

Historically, landfill has been the dominant method of disposing of waste in the UK and many other countries. The process was relatively cheap and there are many worked-out quarries and other mineral extraction sites where the underlying geology provides a natural barrier to protect groundwaters from leachate (discussed later in this chapter). The introduction of the landfill tax and the landfill directive mean that the situation is now changing.

Refer back to Section 2.2 to remind yourself of the national strategies for moving away from landfill.

However, it is important to remember that there will always be a need for some landfill capacity and, at the time of writing, the UK still landfills two thirds of its municipal waste and 55% of its commercial and industrial waste.

In this section, we will look at the chemical and biological processes taking place in an MSW landfill and at the potential for pollution arising from these processes. We will then consider the design and operation of modern landfills and the techniques used to minimize the risk of harm to the environment.

The processes that we will be studying in the following paragraphs also occur in the processes of anaerobic digestion (AD) and waste composting. AD and composting of MSW are considered in Chapters 10 and 11 respectively, and the use of AD in sewage treatment is covered in Block 3.

You will also need to be familiar with the organic chemistry that you studied in Block 0: *Chemistry*. In particular make sure that you are familiar with the principal types of organic polymers.

It is important to note that landfills were intended to be a final disposal point for wastes and were not designed as reactors to break down the wastes. The fact that degradation takes place can be regarded as a side-effect of the materials and conditions present in the site. The chemical and biological processes described in the next section are responsible for landfill's potential to cause pollution through the discharge of the liquid and gaseous products from the degradation processes. The measures described in Section 8.3 are intended to prevent or control these potential pollutants.

8.1   Landfill chemistry and biology

As we have seen in Chapter 3, domestic waste can be divided principally into 60% organic biodegradable materials (paper, kitchen and garden waste, and textiles) and 40% non-biodegradable materials (glass, metals, plastics and minerals). In looking at the processes and reactions that take place in an MSW landfill site we need to concentrate on the biodegradable material, which is where virtually all the chemical and biological changes take place.

So far we have thought about waste composition in terms of the materials present (paper, plastics, glass, etc.). In Block 0: *Chemistry* and in Chapter 9 of this block ('Incineration or energy from wastes') we will be looking at the elemental composition of waste (carbon, hydrogen, sulphur, etc.). But to understand the biological processes involved in the digestion of waste, we need to look at both the chemical composition and the structure at the molecular level.

From the biological point of view, the biodegradable material in waste can be considered to be made up of:

■ *carbohydrates* – simple ones such as sugars, and more complex polymers (e.g. cellulose, the main component of plant cell walls) that consist of a chain of several thousand glucose units;

■ lipids, or fats, which can be thought of as long hydrocarbon chains with a carboxylic acid group at one end;

■ *proteins*, generally also in the form of complex polymers made up of amino acid groups;

■ *lignin*, the organic polymer that holds together plant cell walls and cellulose fibres and which, due to its complex molecular structure, is only very slowly degraded in the AD process.

STUDY NOTE

At this point it may be useful to refer back to the organic chemistry section of Block 0: *Chemistry*.

The decomposition of landfilled waste can be considered in five phases. These are described below.

Phase 1: Aerobic degradation

When waste is first deposited in a landfill site, air is present in the gaps between waste particles, so conditions are described as 'aerobic'. There is also a plentiful supply of water and the nutrients essential for the growth of micro-organisms. Under these conditions aerobic micro-organisms become active and start to degrade the waste in a series of hydrolysis reactions similar to those that take place during waste composting (this is considered in Section 11.6). Readily degradable carbohydrates are broken down into simple sugars (such as glucose), carbon dioxide and water.

These aerobic decomposition reactions are exothermic (heat is generated) so the aerobic phase is accompanied by a rise in temperature, with the final value depending on the amount of oxygen present. The initial oxygen level depends on how tightly the waste is compacted. High compaction rates lead to smaller amounts of air being incorporated within the waste. Peak temperatures are usually in the range 45–70 °C, but uncompacted waste can reach 90 °C. If the waste reaches this high temperature there is the added benefit that many pathogenic organisms in the waste are killed.

However, these aerobic conditions do not last for long. As soon as the waste is deposited it is compacted and shortly afterwards it is covered with more waste or an inert layer of cover material. After a few days (or weeks in uncompacted wastes) the combination of compaction, covering and aerobic activity soon reduces the oxygen levels so the aerobic micro-organisms become inactive and anaerobic conditions begin to develop.

aerobic

exothermic

anaerobic

Phase 2: Hydrolysis and fermentation

As Phase 1 comes to an end, facultative anaerobes (aerobic micro-organisms that can also live in anaerobic conditions) become important. These micro-organisms break down carbohydrates and lipids into sugars in a series of *hydrolysis* reactions that can be summarized by

$$(C_6H_{10}O_4)_n + nH_2O \longrightarrow nC_6H_{12}O_5$$

The sugars are then broken down into carbon dioxide and water by *fermentation*.

We can think of a typical lipid molecule as consisting of a glycerol molecule with three alkane chains attached by ester functional groups (as shown in Figure 20 of Block 0: Chemistry, p33). Hydrolysis of the alkane chains takes place in a number of stages. At each stage the hydrocarbon chains are reduced by one unit in length, so releasing a molecule of acetic acid. We can summarise this process as:

$$2CH_3(CH_2)^n + 2H_2O \longrightarrow 2CH_3(CH_2)^{n-1} + CH_3COOH + 4H^+$$

Proteins consist of long chains of amino acids (a hydrocarbon base containing an amino group and a carboxyl group) (Figure 8). Proteins are first broken down into simpler amino acids; some of these amino acids are then incorporated into the growing mass of micro-organisms while others are further degraded to ammonia and fatty acids (such as acetic acid).

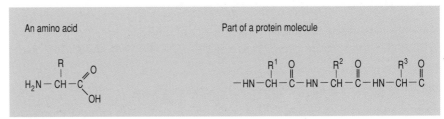

Figure 8   Protein molecule

Gas and leachate formation become more important during Phase 2. The leachates formed during this period are characterized by high ammonium content, and the gas composition can contain up to 80% carbon dioxide and up to 20% hydrogen, with nitrogen making up the remainder. The temperature of the waste falls during this phase to 30–50 °C.

Phase 3: Acetogenesis

In this phase, anaerobic conditions are fully established. 'Acetogenic' micro-organisms convert the organic acids formed in Phase 2 into simpler organic acids (principally acetic acid), acid derivatives, carbon dioxide and hydrogen. Other organisms act on the carbohydrates produced in the hydrolysis reactions to produce more acetic acid in a reaction that can be summarized as

$$C_6H_{12}O_6 + 2H_2O \longrightarrow 2CH_3COOH + 2CO_2 + 4H_2$$

Other reactions involving more complex carbohydrates, carbon dioxide and hydrogen also produce acetic acid while reducing carbon dioxide and hydrogen levels in the gas phase.

The leachate produced during this stage is highly acidic with a pH as low as 4. Under these conditions metal solubility increases, so the leachate also contains high levels of metals.

As the hydrogen and carbon dioxide levels decline the methane-forming micro-organisms (or methanogens) become more active and conditions reach Phase 4.

Phase 4: Methanogenesis

This phase does not normally begin until at least six months after tipping of the waste and it can take a number of years for methanogenic conditions to become fully established.

In this stage, methanogens become more active and generate methane and carbon dioxide from the acetic acid:

$$2CH_3COOH \longrightarrow 2CH_4 + 2CO_2$$

At the same time, carbon dioxide and hydrogen (generated during the hydrolysis of lipids) are combined by other methanogenic bacteria to generate additional methane:

$$4H_2 + CO_2 \longrightarrow CH_4 + 2H_2O$$

The final gaseous product contains about 60% methane and 40% carbon dioxide.

The methane concentration reaches significant levels from 3 to 12 months after the start of the phase and can continue for 15 to 30 years after the final closure of the site. However, small quantities of gas may continue to be produced for up to 100 years after deposition.

The breakdown of the organic acids results in an increase of the leachate pH and the temperature of the waste can range from 30 to 65 °C.

Phase 5: Oxidation

Once the organic acid production and degradation begins to cease, methane and carbon dioxide production slows down and air begins to diffuse into the mass of waste. Aerobic conditions are established and under these conditions, the residual methane is oxidized by the action of aerobic bacteria.

Diagrams showing the progress of each phase and the gas and leachate composition profiles are shown in Figures 9 and 10.

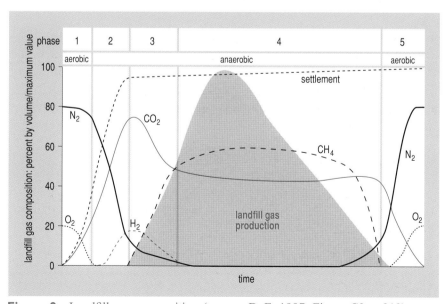

Figure 9 Landfill gas composition (source: DoE, 1997, Figure C3, p.219)

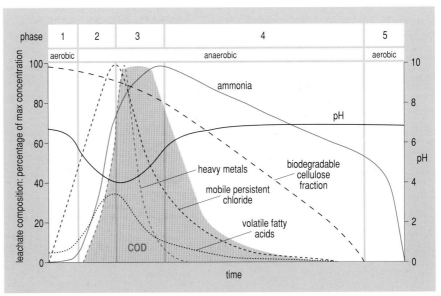

Figure 10 Leachate composition (source: DoE, 1997, Figure C4)

8.2 Landfill site selection

Identifying suitable sites for landfills is a long and complex process involving many stages and consultations. In summary, a suitable site would:

- be located close enough to the source of the waste to satisfy the proximity principle and to keep transport costs to acceptable levels;

- be provided with suitable road (and possibly rail or river) access;

- not be in, or near, a site of special scientific interest (SSSI), area of outstanding natural beauty (AONB), or other protected environment;

- not be located in a sensitive groundwater location if it is to take biodegradable wastes;

- have an owner willing to sell or lease the land to a waste management company.

Once a site has been identified that satisfies all these criteria, the geological and hydrogeological properties need to be evaluated by means of surveys. A typical hydrogeological survey would determine:

- the depth of the *water table*;

- water table contour maps for different seasons of the year;

- the magnitude of annual water table fluctuations;

- the location and distance to points of water use;

- the nature of the local geology;

- the nature of overlying soil;

- the depth of the *unsaturated zone*.

8.3 Landfill site design

Under the requirements of the landfill directive (discussed in Chapter 2), landfill sites must be classified as either inert waste, non-hazardous or hazardous waste sites. Regardless of the classification, sites must:

- be designed to prevent groundwater, surface water and precipitation from entering the site;

- be designed to collect contaminated surface waters for treatment;

- be provided with a geological barrier to prevent water ingress and leachate escape;

- be provided with an artificial sealing liner and drainage layer to collect leachate;

- have a gas collection system and the gas must be used for energy production or be flared.

The precise requirements will vary from site to site and depend on the nature of the waste to be deposited and the local geology and hydrogeological conditions. The liner and capping systems will be selected on the basis of a risk assessment exercise and consultation with the appropriate regulatory body. The landfill directive also specifies minimum requirements for the different classes of landfill.

8.3.1   Site liner

Site liners need to be designed on a site-by-site basis and part of the design process will involve undertaking a risk assessment of the fate of any discharged leachate through a given liner. This risk assessment would take account of local conditions such as hydrogeology and the presence and sensitivity of any aquifers or surface waters. The nature of the waste to be deposited should also be taken into account along with the predicted properties of the leachate (in particular whether it is likely to corrode any part of the lining system).

Having said that, a typical landfill site liner system would consist of the following.

Leachate collection layer

This layer is immediately below the deposited waste and is intended to provide a free-draining region. The layer consists of a 0.5 m thick layer of porous material such as gravel. A network of perforated pipes in this layer leads to a leachate sump to provide drainage. The collected leachate is then pumped out of the sump for treatment at the surface.

Liner protection layer

This layer lies immediately below the leachate collection layer and consists of a flexible geotextile layer. This is a fabric-type material made from polypropylene or polyester fibre polymer membrane. Its purpose is to act as a filter to retain fine material in the drainage layer and to protect the main barrier from being punctured by sharp edges in the gravel that forms the leachate collection layer.

Artificial sealing liner

Together with the geological barrier, the artificial sealing liner prevents leachate from leaving the site and surface waters from entering it. Typically it consists of a polymer membrane together with a layer of compacted natural clay or bentonite-enriched soil – a clay soil with bentonite (a mixture of clay minerals) added to reduce the permeability of the soil. In some instances there may also be a groundwater collection system located below the liner to reduce the risk of groundwater ingress (Figure 11).

Geological barrier

The geological barrier is the geological formation between the underside of the artificial sealing liner and any groundwater that may be present. It will consist of low-permeability material to prevent any harm to the soil or groundwater in the long term after the artificial sealing liner has degraded.

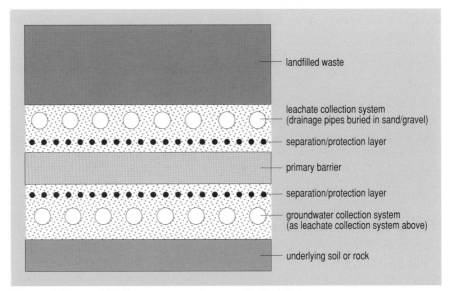

Figure 11   Landfill liner structure (source: DoE, 1997)

Even with the most carefully prepared lining system there will always be some seepage which may be calculated using Darcy's law. Darcy's law is used to predict the flow of fluids through beds of granular material and can be expressed in the following way

$$Q = kAi$$

or

$$\frac{Q}{A} = ki$$

where Q is the flow rate in cubic metres per day, k is the permeability in metres per day (a measure of how rapidly a fluid will flow through the granular bed), i is the ***hydraulic gradient*** (defined as the sum of the head or depth of fluid and the thickness of the geological barrier, divided by the thickness of the geological barrier) and A is the cross-sectional area in square metres perpendicular to the flow.

I will explain the use of this equation by means of the following example. Consider a landfill site with an area of 2500 m^2 lined with 1.5 m of compacted homogeneous clay having a permeability of 10^{-9} m d^{-1}. If leachate pumping limits the head of leachate to 2 m, what is the annual flow of leachate from the site?

The hydraulic gradient (i) of leachate across the clay layer is

$$i = \frac{\text{leachate depth} + \text{thickness of clay layer}}{\text{clay thickness}} = \frac{2 + 1.5}{1.5} = 2.333$$

so Q can be expressed as

$$Q = 10^{-9} \times 2500 \times 2.333 \ \text{m}^3 \ \text{d}^{-1}$$

$$= 5.83 \times 10^{-6} \ \text{m}^3 \ \text{d}^{-1}$$

$$= 2.13 \times 10^{-3} \ \text{m}^3 \ \text{year}^{-1}$$

or

$$Q = 8.52 \times 10^{-7} \ \text{m}^3 \ \text{year}^{-1} \text{ per square metre of the base of the landfill}$$

SAQ 13

Produce a graph showing how the annual flow of leachate from the site varies with the depth of leachate from 0.5 m to 5 m.

The graph (and the equation) demonstrate that leachate flow is directly proportional to the depth of leachate in the cell. This is why it is important to maintain low leachate levels.

SAQ 14

Plot a similar graph to demonstrate the effect of permeability on the leachate flows (take values of permeability from $1 \times 10^{-7} \ \text{m} \ \text{d}^{-1}$ to $1 \times 10^{-9} \ \text{m} \ \text{d}^{-1}$).

8.3.2 Site capping

On completion of tipping, each cell must be capped. This is necessary for several reasons:

- to contain and protect the waste from vermin, and the weather;

- to control the entry of rainwater and surface water into the site;

- to assist in the control of fugitive emissions of landfill gas;

- to control the ingress of air which may disrupt the anaerobic conditions.

As is the case with the lining, the precise requirements for the cap will depend on local conditions and the type of waste deposited (as described in Section 8.3.1). Typically, the cap will consist of five layers. Working upwards from the layer immediately above the surface of the waste, these layers are as follows:

Surface gas drainage layer
A layer of porous material that allows gas to migrate laterally under the action of pumps provided at the edge of the site.

Surface artificial sealing liner
A membrane or geotextile layer used to prevent the ingress of water. This is a requirement for hazardous waste sites where preventing the ingress of water is crucial. It is not normally required for other types of site.

Impermeable mineral surface layer
A layer of compacted clay generally used in all types of landfill to protect the artificial sealing layer (where used) and to reduce water ingress and gas escape.

Surface drainage layer
This layer is immediately above the mineral layer and is designed to allow the free flow of water to the site perimeter where it can be collected in drainage channels.

Topsoil cover

Finally, all sites require a restoration layer of topsoil to protect the capping layers and allow grasses and other plants to be established without the danger of roots penetrating the mineral layer and creating channels for water ingress or gas escape. In addition, if the soil cover is well-aerated and contains sufficient organic matter, this promotes the growth of microbial communities which are able to oxidize any methane that seeps through the capping layers.

8.3.3   Surface water protection

The lining systems discussed above have a primary aim of preventing the pollution of the surrounding land and any aquifers present. However, it is also important to protect any surface waters within the site.

Running water

If a stream runs through the landfill site, diversion prior to landfill is required as a precaution against the occurrence of water pollution. If the site is near a river bank diversion is not possible. In this case, an impervious seal must be inserted between the site and the river bank.

Static water

Precautions must also be taken to prevent static water becoming polluted by tipping. Static water is often encountered in old workings, such as clay pits and quarries. The water should be pumped out prior to landfill, but often this is not, or cannot be, done. In such cases, the procedure is to infill with inert material (e.g. hardcore) for several metres above the water table to provide an unsaturated base; landfill may then commence.

Run-off

Rainfall and any other water entering the site area can potentially pick up pollutants ranging from roadway dust through to landfill leachate. Therefore all site surface waters must be collected and prevented from draining into watercourses. Depending on the degree of contamination, this water can be treated in reed beds (which you met in Block 3) or by combining with the leachate for treatment as described in the next section.

8.3.4   Leachate collection and treatment

There are three main reasons why landfill site licences require the removal of leachate that accumulates in the base of a landfill site:

■   to reduce leakage; the lower the 'head' of leachate, the lower the leakage rate through the site liner (as we saw in Section 8.3.1);

■   to reduce damage to the liner from corrosive substances in the leachate;

■   to allow the leachate to be treated so it can be discharged to sewers or watercourses without harm to the environment.

Leachate is collected in sumps across the site. These sumps consist of low points that are formed by careful contouring of the base of the site. Leachate tends to drain into these sumps by gravity, and drainage is also assisted by the leachate collection layer described in Section 8.3.1. A vertical well leads from the bottom of each sump to the surface. Each well is fitted with pipes and pumps to remove the leachate for treatment.

The leachate treatment processes used depend on the amount of leachate produced, its composition and the standard that must be reached before the leachate can be discharged. The processes used are based on those used to treat sewage and are discussed in detail in Block 3. Refer to this block for details of each technology, but at this stage you should be aware of the following treatment processes:

- air stripping to remove ammonia;

- coagulation, flocculation and settling to remove heavy metals and suspended solids;

- aerobic biological treatment;

- biological contactors that use aerobic micro-organisms to break down organic compounds;

- adsorption of low levels of organic contaminants on activated carbon;

- reverse osmosis to remove suspended solids, ammonium compounds, heavy metals and to reduce COD and BOD. This is used for leachates with a high inorganic loading and low rates of formation. (Note that this is only a concentration process which generates a concentrated liquid by-product that needs treatment – usually after transport in tankers to sewage treatment works);

- distillation (this process also generates a concentrated liquor requiring off-site treatment);

- oxidation with hydrogen peroxide or other oxidizing agents to treat sulphur compounds and some organic compounds;

- oxidation of high organic content leachates with air at high temperature and pressure (known as 'wet air oxidation');

- anaerobic treatment that uses anaerobic micro-organisms to degrade the organic compounds to methane and carbon dioxide (a controlled version of the reactions taking place in the landfill itself);

- reed bed treatment to process lightly contaminated leachates.

Currently, leachate is usually treated on site by coagulation/settlement followed by aerobic treatment before being discharged to a watercourse, but may be discharged to a sewer or taken by tanker to a sewage treatment works. At some landfill sites the leachate is only partially treated and is then injected back into the site through a network of pipes or sprayed onto the site surface. Reinjection can lead to a more rapid breakdown of the waste and higher rates of landfill gas production. You should note that, as the landfill directive takes effect, leachate characteristics and treatment methods will change.

8.3.5 Landfill gas collection and treatment

The site lining and capping systems that we discussed above play important roles in preventing the uncontrolled discharge of landfill gas from a site. As the gas has no means of escape a gas removal system is required. This normally consists of a network of vertical boreholes connected to a network of pipes at the surface and a system of pumps.

The collected gas is passed through a condensate trap to remove any water droplets. The gas is then burned either in an engine driving a generator to produce power or in a boiler to produce steam for power generation. Alternatively, it is burned in a flare stack.

Flaring converts the methane to carbon dioxide (a much less potent greenhouse gas) and destroys odour-forming compounds. It is generally used at sites that do not produce sufficient gas to make investment in energy recovery plant worthwhile. Flares are also installed at sites with energy recovery for use as a back-up during maintenance or breakdown of the energy generation plant.

Where sufficient volumes of gas are produced a gas engine or boiler is installed to generate power from the gas. At the time of writing there are over 100 sites fitted with energy recovery equipment in the UK (principally power generation using gas engines) producing a total of 600 MW of power.

Although engines and flares control the explosive hazards associated with methane and replace methane with carbon dioxide, a much less potent greenhouse gas, they generate pollutants in their own right as shown in Table 13.

Table 13   Landfill gas combustion plant emissions

Pollutant	Dual fuel diesel engine $(mg\ m^{-3})$	Spark ignition engine $(mg\ m^{-3})$	Gas turbine $(mg\ m^{-3})$
Particulate matter	4.3	125	9
Carbon monoxide	800	10 000	14
Unburned hydrocarbons	22	>200	15
Nitrogen oxides	795	1170	61
Hydrogen chloride	12	15	38
Sulphur dioxide	51	22	6

Source: Williams (1998).

8.4   Site layout and operation

Detailed guidance on the layout and operation of landfill sites is given in DoE (1997). For full details you should consult this reference, but the key points are summarized in the following sections.

8.4.1   Site layout

The layout of a typical landfill site is shown in Figure 12. Most of the features shown are self-explanatory, but you should note the following essential aspects of all landfill sites:

■ the perimeter fence and secured site entrance;

■ site office buildings;

■ waste inspection facilities and laboratory;

■ weighbridges to record weights of all vehicles entering and leaving the site;

■ garages and workshops;

■ clear signs and directions to drivers and other site users;

■ wheel cleaning facilities at site exit;

■ leachate and contaminated water treatment facilities.

8.4.2   Waste emplacement

On arrival at the site, the vehicle containing the waste will be weighed and the load and documentation inspected. The vehicle will then be directed to the tipping area to discharge its load. On leaving the active area of the site the vehicle will pass through a wheel washer and be reweighed to determine the weight of waste deposited. The weight data are used for charging purposes, to assess the site's liability for landfill tax and possibly for use in monitoring compliance with the landfill directive.

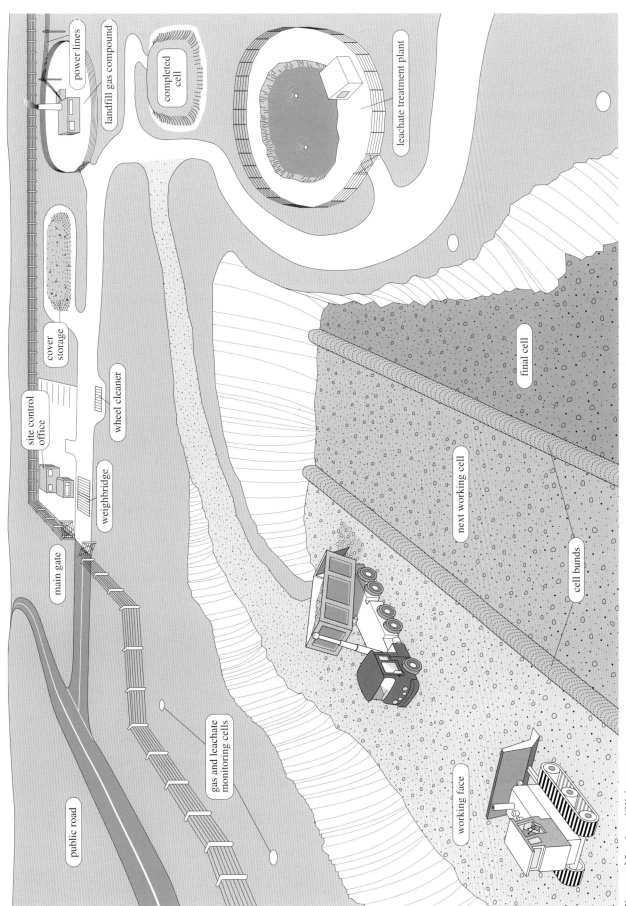

power lines

landfill gas compound

completed cell

leachate treatment plant

site control office

cover storage

wheel cleaner

weighbridge

main gate

final cell

next working cell

cell bunds

public road

gas and leachate monitoring cells

working face

Figure 12 Landfill layout

The waste discharged in the tipping area is compacted by means of a steel-wheeled compaction vehicle and at the end of each working day the tipping area is usually covered with a layer of inert waste or soil. This daily cover material is used to help suppress dispersion of the waste by the wind and discourages seagulls and rodents from visiting the site.

Landfill sites are normally filled on a phased basis where a given area is filled over 12–18 months and then capped. Filling then moves to another part of the site. This practice keeps the working area to a minimum and means that waste is covered and capped in as short a time as possible. This reduces the amount of rainfall entering the deposited wastes and also reduces the time before usable quantities of landfill gas are produced and minimizes odours from the site.

8.4.3   Environmental controls

We have already discussed the main potential environmental hazards associated with landfill, namely leachate and landfill gas. In addition to these pollutants of national or international importance it is vital to take measures to control pollution at the more local level, for example:

■ vehicle movements to and from the site;

■ noise from operating vehicles;

■ dust from waste tipping, vehicle movements and the transport and use of cover material;

■ windblown litter;

■ odours;

■ vermin (particularly gulls and rats).

8.4.4   Site restoration and aftercare

Once a landfill has been completed, the site operator is still responsible for the care and maintenance of the site. In particular, the operator is responsible for the prevention of any pollution from landfill gas or leachate. This responsibility (and financial liability) continues until the operator can satisfy the national regulator that the site will not pose a threat to the environment even if left unattended. For a site taking biodegradable waste, it may take up to 100–200 years before this stable state is reached.

8.5   Summary

Landfill has been the predominant method of managing wastes in the UK and overseas and this is likely to continue even with the changes due to the national waste strategies and the landfill directive.

Once landfilled, organic waste undergoes a series of biological degradation processes, principally under anaerobic (oxygen-free) conditions. These processes lead to the production of landfill gas and contaminated leachate with potentially serious environmental and public health impacts.

Landfill sites are designed to prevent the uncontrolled emissions of leachate and gas to the environment. The impermeable liner prevents the escape of leachate into ground waters and also the sideways migration of gas. An impermeable cap prevents the escape of gas into the atmosphere and the entry of water into the mass of waste thus reducing leachate formation.

Drainage systems are used to collect leachate which is then either treated on-site before being discharged into rivers, or discharged without treatment to sewers or taken by tanker for off-site treatment. The gas is collected using a network of wells and is either burned in an engine or boiler for energy recovery, or burned in a flare. This reduces the risk of methane explosions and the global warming potential of the emissions.

Landfill sites remain active for many years (possibly 50 years or longer) after filling has been completed. Throughout this period the operator is responsible for ensuring that the site does not cause any environmental pollution.

Landfills are necessary and can be operated with minimal adverse environmental impact. However, they do not contribute to the conservation of resources (with the exception of a small amount of energy recovery) and their long active lives mean that they will leave problems for future generations to solve. For these reasons, landfills cannot be regarded as presenting a sustainable way of managing waste.

9   INCINERATION OR ENERGY FROM WASTES

In the previous chapter, we recognized the importance of landfill in managing our wastes, but we also identified many potential problems – from long-term potential for pollution to the low potential for recovering anything of value from the waste. One solution may be to burn the waste and recover the energy and this forms the subject of this chapter.

9.1   Introduction

I will begin this section by clarifying the terms 'energy from waste' and 'incineration'. Incineration is the combustion process used to reduce the volume of waste for final disposal or to reduce its toxicity and the process may or may not recover any of the heat released. 'Energy from waste' (EfW) is a type of incineration process in which boilers or other heat recovery systems are used to recover the energy from the combustion gases for use in power or heat generation. All MSW incinerators in the developed world now operate as EfW facilities.

In many textbooks and articles in the press you will see the terms used interchangeably, but more often than not the term 'incineration' is favoured. For the sake of brevity, I will also adopt this convention, but you should take it that, unless otherwise stated, MSW incineration is always associated with EfW.

We can define MSW incineration as:

> the combustion of waste under controlled conditions and with the removal of potential pollutants from the combustion gases.

I have already stated that energy is recovered, but ferrous and non-ferrous metals are also reclaimed from the residual ash. In many cases, parts of the ash can be recycled as an aggregate substitute in road building and for other construction purposes.

Therefore, the principal benefit of energy from waste is that it achieves a 90% reduction in the volume of material to be disposed of to landfill. Other benefits are the savings in fossil fuel and the recycling of metals and aggregates.

The main disbenefit of incineration is that it is often difficult to obtain planning authorization for the development of new schemes due to public opposition. This opposition often relates to people's perceptions of the previous generation of incinerators that operated to very low environmental standards. Pollutant emissions that were tolerated then would be unacceptable today. A lot of this opposition is related to concerns over dioxin emissions. You looked at dioxins in Block 1 in the context of the risks to public health. Their control is discussed later in this chapter.

Another source of opposition comes from single-issue pressure groups organized on a transnational basis. These groups tend to be opposed to what they perceive as our 'throw-away consumer society' and see waste management in general and incineration in particular as a key symptom of what is wrong with our current lifestyle. While these organizations do have a valid point they tend to ignore the fact that we, as consumers, have a choice. Most of us make that choice and buy goods and services that may be wasteful, but which are convenient or give us pleasure.

The main technical problem associated with incineration is that the process produces a small quantity (about 30 kg per tonne of waste treated) of material from the pollution abatement plant that is classed as a hazardous waste (see Chapter 5), which must be disposed of in tightly controlled landfill sites.

9.2   Incineration across Europe

Table 14 shows the extent to which incineration with energy recovery is used across the EU. For comparison, recycling and landfill rates are also given.

Table 14   Incineration across the European Union

	Energy recovery	Recycling and composting	Landfill
Austria	11	59	30
Belgium	36	52	13
Denmark	54	41	5
Finland	9	28	63
France	34	28	38
Germany	23	57	20
Greece	0	9	91
Ireland	0	31	69
Italy	9	29	62
Luxembourg	41	36	23
Netherlands	33	64	3
Portugal	22	4	74
Spain	7	34	59
Sweden	45	41	14
United Kingdom	8	18	74

Source: Defra (2006b).

The key points to draw from Table 14 are that energy recovery through incineration is a well-established technology and that high recycling rates can be compatible with high energy recovery rates.

There are 19 incinerators operating across the UK (see Table 15). These range from the two very large plants in London to a small facility in Lerwick treating waste generated on the island where landfill is limited and export to the mainland would be prohibitively expensive. With the implementation of the landfill directive (see Chapter 2) a number of new plants are expected to be built over the period 2000 to 2020.

Table 15   UK MSW incineration plants

Location	Capacity (tonnes y^{-1})
North London (Edmonton)	600 000
Allington (Kent)	500 000
South London (Lewisham)	420 000
Birmingham	350 000
Cleveland	245 000
Sheffield	225 000
Coventry	200 000
Stoke	200 000
Marchwood	165 000
Portsmouth	165 000
Nottingham	150 000
Kirklees	135 000
Bolton	130 000
Dundee	120 000
Wolverhampton	105 000
Dudley	90 000
Basingstoke	90 000
Grimsby	56 000
Lerwick	26 000
Total	3 972 000

9.3   Incineration regulation

All MSW incinerators in England and Wales are required to meet emission limits and operational controls specified by the Environment Agency under the system of integrated pollution prevention and control (IPPC) (similar, but separate arrangements are in force in Scotland and Northern Ireland). This implements the EU directives on IPPC and incineration. Under IPPC, plant operators must demonstrate that they are applying the principle of 'best available techniques' (BAT) to prevent, or where not practicable, to minimize pollution. In particular they must demonstrate that:

■ no significant pollution will be caused;

■ waste production is avoided and, where waste is produced, energy is recovered (where this is not possible it is disposed of in a way that has the least impact on the environment);

■ energy is used efficiently;

■ measures are taken to avoid accidents and limit their consequences;

■ measures are taken on closure of the installation to avoid pollution and return the site to an acceptable condition.

Although BAT will, in part, depend on local circumstances the European Commission has drafted a series of BAT Reference Documents (BREF notes) that will be used by Member States in drawing up their own guidance notes for emission limits and operating requirements.

Table 16 shows the emission limits based on the directive.

Table 16 UK waste combustion emission limits

Component	EU directive (December 2000) (mg m^{-3})	
	24-hourly average	0.5-hourly average
Dust	10	30
Total organic carbon	10	20
CO	50	100
Dioxins (I-TEQ)	0.1^a	–
HCl	10	60
HF	1	4
SO_x	50	200
NO_x	200	400
NO_x (small plant)	400	–
NH_3	10	20
Hg	0.05	–
Cd + Tl	0.05	–
Sb + As + Pb + Cr + Co + Cu + Mn + Ni + V + Sn	0.5	–

^{a}Emission limits for dioxins (I-TEQ) are given in ng m^{-3}.

In addition, the operators of proposed plants must obtain planning permission from the local planning authority. In the case of major projects (including incinerators) the application must be accompanied by an environmental statement based on an *environmental impact assessment*. This statement should describe all the potential impacts on all aspects of the environment and how any significant adverse effects will be avoided or reduced.

The planning authority's role is to ensure that there is no significant clash between domestic, commercial, industrial, agricultural or aesthetic interests. Pollution impacts are not of prime concern, but are taken into account by the planning authority.

The siting and granting of planning permission for any type of waste management facility is a controversial issue. For this reason the final decision is often taken by the Secretary of State for the Environment after holding a public enquiry. Such an enquiry can last for several months and entail the very high costs associated with employing solicitors, barristers and expert witnesses for an extended period of time.

9.4   Incineration technology

9.4.1   Mass burn systems

Mass burn systems take the entire waste stream and burn it with virtually no pre-processing. Most commercial systems throughout the world operate in this way. A typical mass burn incinerator is shown in Figure 13 and is described in the following paragraphs. (Also, see the Set Book entry on *incineration*.)

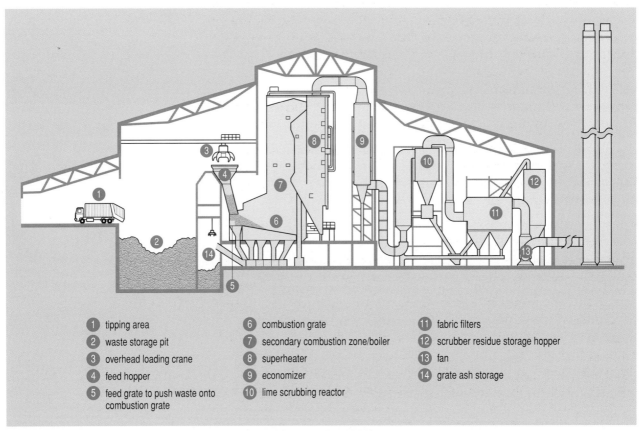

1 tipping area	**6** combustion grate	**11** fabric filters
2 waste storage pit	**7** secondary combustion zone/boiler	**12** scrubber residue storage hopper
3 overhead loading crane	**8** superheater	**13** fan
4 feed hopper	**9** economizer	**14** grate ash storage
5 feed grate to push waste onto combustion grate	**10** lime scrubbing reactor	

Figure 13   Mass burn incinerator (source: adapted from SITA, 2002)

The waste is discharged from the collection vehicles into a storage pit. The pit acts as a storage area to allow for the fact that the incinerator operates for 24 hours per day and only shuts down once a year for inspection and maintenance over a 1–2 week period. Therefore the pit must be able to store sufficient waste to keep the plant operating over weekends and public holidays.

The pit also allows the operators to mix the waste with a grab crane to keep its properties as uniform as possible. For example, a load of paper-rich commercial waste could be mixed with a load containing large amounts of wet food-processing wastes that have low calorific value. This mixing helps to keep the output from the boiler constant, but also maintains constant furnace conditions, which helps to minimize pollutant formation. The grab crane is also used to transfer waste from the pit to the furnace feed chute.

The waste passes through the chute under gravity and the plug of waste also acts as a seal to prevent the ingress of air into the furnace. Once on the grate, the waste is heated by radiation from the furnace walls and moisture is driven off. On further heating the waste begins to pyrolyse (see *pyrolysis* in the Set Book) and volatile compounds are given off and burned above the grate. The remaining material moves further down the grate and the residual carbonaceous material continues to burn slowly, before the ash is discharged from the end of the grate into a water-filled quench tank. This tank quenches any remaining combustion reactions, causes large clinker to shatter into smaller pieces and prevents the entry of air into the furnace.

The efficiency of the incineration grate system – defined by the consumption of carbon in the waste – depends on its ability to provide the correct amount of combustion air to each section of the grate. It is important to ensure that there is a high pressure drop through the grate so that any variability in waste loading on the grate does not cause a shift of air away from a particular part of the grate. The grate is also responsible for agitating the burning mass of waste to ensure that complete combustion is achieved. Several different designs of grate are currently used in MSW incinerators, but the forward and reverse-acting reciprocating grates, as well as the rotary drum (or roller) grates, are most frequently applied in modern incinerators.

Reciprocating grates have very good primary air distribution and the quality of the waste burn-out is generally excellent. However, they have a high number of moving parts, so they suffer more wear and have slightly shorter lifetimes than rotary drum grates.

Advantages of the rotary drum grate are the flexibility in waste transport speed and a relatively good durability of the grate bars. The main disadvantage, however, is that fouling between bars and wear of scrapers between the drum can cause difficulties with the primary air supply.

The furnace or combustion chamber is the region above the grate where combustion of the volatile matter takes place. The volatile matter that leaves the waste bed is rich in carbon monoxide (CO) and hydrogen, and contains high concentrations of unburned hydrocarbons. The size and shape of the chamber are important in directing some of the heat of the fire (through radiation and convection) back onto the fuel bed to ensure drying and ignition of the waste. Secondary (overfire) air is injected into the flame region to provide additional oxygen and generate turbulence. This ensures that combustion of the volatile matter is completed. The furnace geometry is also responsible for ensuring mixing of the combustible gases with air to ensure complete burn-out of the waste. Adequate gas mixing and residence time within the combustion chamber will prevent cold spots, which can cause lower gas-phase reactions and an increase in emissions of CO and unburned hydrocarbons.

A typical heat recovery system consists of four sections:

- a radiant water wall to recover heat from the flame zone of the furnace;

- a superheater section which produces superheated steam from the saturated steam (see *superheating* in the Set Book);

- a convective section of the boiler which removes the majority of the heat from the combustion gases and generates saturated steam from the feedwater;

- an economizer section which is used to heat the incoming boiler feedwater before it enters the convective section.

Generally, the flue gas temperatures through the boiler depend upon the sizes of the heat recovery sections and the steam conditions required for the power generation plant or process use. Typically, the temperature in the furnace is around 1150–1450 °C which is subsequently reduced by heat transfer to the boiler sections to 200–250 °C. Steam conditions in the boiler are restricted so that tube surface temperatures are kept below 400–450 °C to avoid excessive corrosion. In general, MSW boilers are designed with steam conditions of 40–45 bar pressure and 400–450 °C.

9.4.2 Fluidized bed systems

In a fluidized bed combustor (FBC), instead of a grate or hearth supporting a bed of solid fuel, the furnace section contains a bed of sand. Air is blown through nozzles in the base of the furnace with a velocity sufficient to 'fluidize' the material. The fluidized bed of sand and air resembles a violently boiling liquid. Beds that operate at these air velocities are known as bubbling fluidized bed (BFB) combustors.

If the air velocity is increased beyond that normally used in BFB combustors the bed becomes more violent and the lighter sand particles are blown out of the bed in the air stream. This is undesirable in BFBs because the bed material is soon all lost. However, circulating fluidized beds (CFBs), which have a system for collecting this entrained sand and returning it to the bed, operate at these high air velocities.

Fluidized beds have a number of potential advantages over conventional grate combustion systems. The large mass of hot bed material means that they can burn wastes with lower calorific values than conventional systems. The bed temperature is lower than that found on conventional grates which means that oxides of nitrogen formation can be reduced (NO_x control is discussed in Section 9.5.4). On the other hand, FBCs are less robust than grate systems and the feedstock must be processed before entering the combustor.

In both BFBs and CFBs, the material is heated to the operating temperature by auxiliary burners. Shredded waste is introduced either by dropping it onto the top of the bed or injecting it from below.

Depending on the design of the BFB, heat transfer is achieved by means of a combination of in-bed heat transfer surfaces, radiant surfaces in the freeboard zone above the bed, and a convective boiler beyond the combustor. A schematic representation of this type of system is shown in Figure 14. The combustor may consist of a simple refractory-lined vessel with an external waste heat boiler. Heat transfer surfaces within the bed are not used where fuel quality is extremely low due to high amounts of non-combustibles or moisture. In extreme cases, auxiliary fuel may be introduced into the bed to sustain combustion and/or bed temperature. This configuration has been widely used to burn sewage sludge with a moisture content of up to 85%.

In the CFB, heat is transferred from the bed material to heating surfaces over the entire height of the combustor or furnace section. Any remaining heat is transferred via a conventional convective section located after the combustor (see Figure 15). By varying the fluidization velocity within the combustor, the amount of heat transfer surface in contact with bed material within the furnace can be varied to control load or temperature.

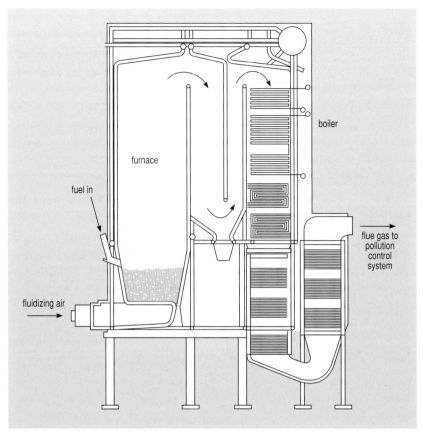

Figure 14 Bubbling fluidized bed furnace

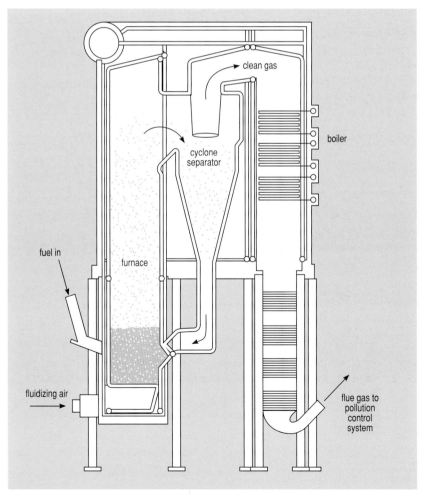

Figure 15 Circulating fluidized bed furnace

Feedstock preparation

All FBCs require some degree of fuel preparation when firing MSW because the fuel itself must be able to be fluidized, or at least be partially supported within the bed for good mixing and combustion. The ability to fluidize a given material at a specific gas flow depends primarily on the material's particle size and density. Large-sized or heavy objects, such as pieces of concrete or steel, would fall to the bottom of the bed if not removed from the feed. If these large items are not removed from the waste or from the operating bed they tend to build up at the bottom of the combustor on the air distributor and are too heavy to be fluidized. In areas where fluidization is lost, the temperature rises, allowing ash to melt and agglomerate into additional large particles causing increased loss of fluidization. The air flows then become disrupted leading to increased CO generation.

The need to prepare the feedstock means that energy from waste encourages materials reclamation. In the feed preparation process metals can be reclaimed by magnetic separation and fine material can be separated out for landfill cover. Also, if markets exist, paper and plastics can be recovered by hand-picking (although there are health, safety and ethical questions over the practice of hand-picking waste). An example of an integrated recycling/pre-treatment process is shown in Figure 16.

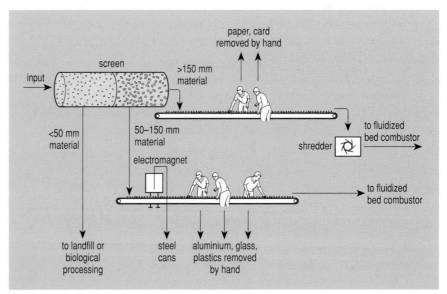

Figure 16   FBC feedstock preparation/recycling system

SAQ 15

Before attempting this question you may wish to revise Chapter 5 of Block 0: Chemistry.

A typical MSW has the following chemical composition: moisture 27%, carbon 24%, hydrogen 3%, oxygen 28%, sulphur 0.1%. (Note that you can assume that the water and the remaining inert materials take no part in the combustion reactions.) Calculate the volume of air required to completely burn 1 tonne of MSW.

If the furnace design means that the amount of air required is 190% of this theoretical amount, calculate the total volume of air required and the principal components of the combustion gases (nitrogen, oxygen, carbon dioxide, water).

Relative atomic masses are: $C = 12$, $H = 1$, $O = 16$, $S = 32$.

Air is 21% oxygen by volume.

1 kmol of any gas occupies 22.4 m^3 under standard conditions.

9.4.3 Advanced thermal conversion systems

Thermolysis

Thermolysis is a generic term increasingly being used to describe emerging energy from waste technologies based on thermochemical treatment, *gasification* or *pyrolysis* of processed refuse (or refuse-derived fuel). In conventional incineration large excess volumes of air are introduced into the combustion zone to aid the combustion process, but in gasification the quantity of air is restricted to that just needed to drive volatile gases from the waste. The gas produced has a medium heating value, and may either be burnt directly to raise steam in a conventional manner, or upgraded to process gas for industrial use or to generate electricity through a gas engine.

In pyrolysis, air is essentially excluded from the process, with the volatile matter being driven from the waste in an externally heated reactor. Generally, a higher quality gas is produced, which again may be used to raise steam or generate electricity.

Pyrolysis systems were originally developed for biomass applications. However, there are now some 40 companies developing or offering MSW-based systems. One of the principal advantages of these over conventional incineration systems is that the volume of air required to combust the waste is greatly reduced, resulting in a significantly smaller (and hence potentially cheaper) gas cleaning plant. Gas cleaning can often be carried out before the final combustion stage, which results in a very much smaller gas cleaning plant and reduced emissions. Also, with lower temperatures than conventional systems, more of the potentially polluting heavy metals are trapped in the ash where they are more amenable to treatment. In the case of pyrolysis this ash is rich in carbon, and it is then relatively straightforward to use vitrification techniques to melt the ash into an inert glass form, rendering it more suitable for disposal or possible reuse.

Thermolysis technology has a number of potential advantages when compared with mass burn technology: plant sizes tend to be smaller, the thermal efficiency is higher and gas cleaning costs can be lower. Also, pressure groups that are fundamentally opposed to mass burn technology appear to have fewer objections to thermolysis.

9.5 Pollution abatement systems

9.5.1 Dry systems

The main pollutants released by the combustion of wastes are the acid gases HCl and SO_2. The simplest way of removing these pollutants is to react them with an alkali. This is done in the dry injection or dry scrubbing process by injecting dry powdered lime (calcium hydroxide – $Ca(OH)_2$) into a reaction tower, or directly into the flue gas downstream of the incinerator boiler outlet.

A flow diagram of a typical dry scrubbing process is shown in Figure 17.

The flue gas components SO_2, HCl and HF react with the lime as follows

$$Ca(OH)_2 + SO_2 \longrightarrow CaSO_3 + H_2O$$

$$Ca(OH)_2 + 2HCl \longrightarrow CaCl_2 + 2H_2O$$

$$Ca(OH)_2 + 2HF \longrightarrow CaF_2 + 2H_2O$$

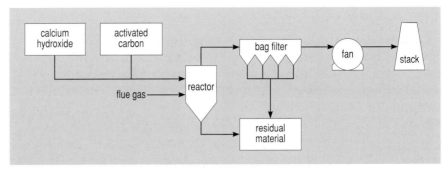

Figure 17   Dry flue gas scrubbing system

To increase the removal efficiency, the flue gas may be first cooled to 160 °C ($\pm$ 20 °C) by injecting water into the flue gas. Cooling in this way also causes condensation of most of the heavy metals, which can subsequently be removed along with the particulate material and unreacted lime in a bag filter or *electrostatic precipitator* (ESP). (ESPs are discussed in Block 6: *Air quality management*.)

A bag filter has the advantage over an ESP because the absorbent builds up on the dust layer on the bags providing an extra opportunity to absorb the acid gases (i.e. less absorbent is needed for the dry system and bag filter combination).

Removal efficiencies for HCl of over 99% are possible. SO_2 removal efficiencies are temperature-dependent but are generally 40% to 60%, unless the temperature is lowered to the dew-point, when the removal efficiency can rise to over 95%. Lead and cadmium removal efficiencies can be better than 99%. Mercury emissions are very temperature-dependent (around 140 °C is required). Capture of mercury can be improved by the injection of activated carbon, fly ash or sodium sulphide with the lime.

Dry systems have been reported to reduce the levels of dioxins, but again this is very temperature-dependent, requiring temperatures as low as 110°C.

The dry system has the advantage of requiring the fewest number of plant items. This reduces the capital cost and increases the reliability of the system. The major disadvantage of the dry system is the large quantity of absorbent that is needed. This not only increases the operating costs of buying the absorbent but also increases the disposal costs. Relatively large amounts of residues are produced, typically 50 kg residue per tonne of MSW incinerated.

SAQ 16

A typical MSW incinerator produces 6000 m³ (under standard conditions) of flue gas per tonne of waste burned. The HCl concentration is 800 ppm and the maximum discharge concentration is 10 mg m⁻³.

Calculate the percentage of the HCl that must be removed from the flue gas, and the theoretical amount of lime ($Ca(OH)_2$) required to achieve this.

Note: 1 kmol of gas occupies 22.4 m³ under standard conditions. Relative atomic masses are as follows: H = 1, Cl = 35.5, Ca = 40, O = 16.

9.5.2 Semi-dry systems

Reacting a solid with a gas is not a particularly efficient process, because it depends on the surface area of solid available for contact. This is not great, even for a fine powder. The process can be made more effective if the alkali is in the form of a liquid and, if the amount of liquid added is selected correctly, complete evaporation occurs. For this reason the process is known as semi-dry scrubbing. In this process (also called the spray dryer process), the scrubbing agent is in the form of a liquid (usually milk of lime, CaO) which is atomized as finely as possible inside a reactor through which the flue gases are passed.

The atomized droplets simultaneously undergo three mass and heat transfer processes:

- mass transfer of acid gases from the gas stream into the droplets;

- chemical reaction between acids and the dissolved lime;

- evaporation of the water in the droplets.

The reagent consumption is reduced by returning a proportion of the solid products to the reactor feed stream. The ratio of recirculated product to fresh CaO depends on the required efficiency of HCl removal, the flue gas quantity and the flue gas temperature (usually 190–300 °C). In general, the lower the temperature the higher the acid gas removal, although an excessively low temperature may cause serious deposition and solids handling problems because the products may become damp from condensation.

The atomized droplets evaporate as they pass down through the reactor tower, leaving a dry powder consisting of calcium chloride, sulphate and sulphite, plus any unreacted calcium hydroxide (approximately 20%). Most of this material is entrained in the flue gas and is removed in a bag filter or an ESP. As in dry scrubbing, the bag filter has the advantage of providing a further stage of scrubbing as the gas passes through the material accumulating on the bag.

Removal efficiencies of over 90% have been quoted for HCl, SO_2 and HF. High mercury removal efficiency requires a low gas temperature and a suitable surface for adsorption to take place. This can be provided by injecting finely powdered activated carbon into the scrubbing tower with the alkali.

Dioxin removal is similarly favoured by low temperatures. Removal efficiencies of over 99% for dioxins have been quoted by manufacturers at temperatures from 110 to 200 °C, but careful control is needed to avoid condensation problems.

The use of an absorbent in liquid form results in a lower *stoichiometric ratio* being required. This produces less residue which must be disposed of (typically 40 kg per tonne MSW combusted). However, operation is slightly more difficult and the capital costs are slightly higher when compared to dry scrubbing.

9.5.3 Wet systems

The wet scrubber process uses a liquid absorbent to wash the flue gases within a reaction tower. Scrubbing often takes place in two stages to optimize the removal of HCl and SO_2. A typical two-stage system is shown in Figure 18 and is described below.

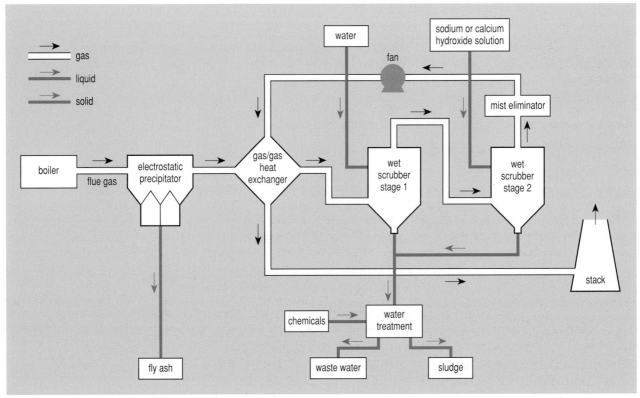

Figure 18   Wet flue gas scrubbing system

First, the bulk of the dust and fly ash is removed from the gas stream in an ESP. The gas is then cooled to 130–150 °C in a heat exchanger. The flue gas then enters the scrubber where it flows up against the flow of recirculating scrubbing water. At the same time the flue gas is cooled to the adiabatic saturation temperature (approximately 60 °C). This initial acid stage absorbs HCl, the remaining dust and condensed heavy metals. The pH drops to 0.5–1, which favours the absorption of heavy metals, particularly mercury.

Adiabatic saturation temperature means the temperature that is reached due to cooling by evaporation of the water until the gas is saturated.

The flue gas then enters the second scrubbing stage, which may be either situated in the top part of the tower or housed in a separate unit. Here it is brought into contact with a sodium or calcium hydroxide solution at a higher pH (7 or more). This absorbs the sulphur dioxide and any remaining HCl.

After removal of droplets of liquid via a mist eliminator, the flue gas is extracted by a booster fan and fed to the heat exchanger where it is reheated by the cooling furnace exit gases to about 100 °C before passing to the stack.

The wet scrubbing system results in the lowest amount of solid residue (typically 20 kg per tonne MSW combusted). However, it does produce a liquid effluent (typically 450 kg per tonne MSW) which requires treatment before disposal.

9.5.4 NOx control

Nitrogen monoxide and nitrogen dioxide (NO and NO_2, collectively referred to as NO_x) are by-products of the combustion process.

The nitrogen can originate from the atmospheric air or from the organic compounds of the fuel. In the first case, the generated NO_x is referred to as 'thermal NO_x' and in the second case as 'fuel NO_x'. The formation of thermal NO_x is greatly dependent on the combustion temperature and the partial pressure of oxygen; it starts at temperatures above 1200 °C and increases rapidly with the temperature, O_2 concentration and the residence time in the high temperature zone. The formation of the fuel NO_x is dependent on the nitrogen content of the fuel.

NO_x emissions can be controlled by primary measures (in the combustion chamber) and secondary measures (flue gas treatment).

Primary methods are used to prevent the formation of NO_x by modifying or improving the combustion process. Excess air levels are reduced and air input is staged by introducing a higher proportion as overfire air. Flue gas recirculation (FGR) is a technique by which a proportion of the cleaned flue gas is recirculated into the combustor replacing combustion air. FGR has the effect of lowering excess oxygen and lowering flame temperatures. Primary methods can achieve NO_x reductions of 10–30% at a minimal cost.

Secondary methods are employed to reduce NO_x levels by treating the NO_x formed in the combustion zone. There are two main technologies: selective non-catalytic reduction (SNCR) and selective catalytic reduction (SCR). Both techniques reduce NO_x to N_2 and water using NH_3 or urea, albeit by different methods. SNCR achieves NO_x reduction by introducing NH_3 or urea into the boiler. SCR uses a catalyst in a catalytic reactor after the flue gas cleaning plant to enhance the performance of the reaction and achieve better results. Secondary methods can achieve NO_x reductions of 50–90%.

SAQ 17

The equation for the reduction of NO_2 by ammonia is

$$2NO_2 + 4NH_3 + O_2 \longrightarrow 3N_2 + 6H_2O$$

A typical incinerator produces 6000 m^3 (at Standard Temperature and Pressure) of combustion gas per tonne of waste burned, with an NO_2 concentration of 400 mg m^{-3}. What is the theoretical (or stoichiometric) amount of ammonia required per tonne of waste burned if the NO_2 concentration of the final emissions must be less than 200 mg m^{-3}?

9.5.5 Dioxin control

Polychlorinated dibenzo-para-dioxins (PCDDs) and polychlorinated dibenzofurans (PCDFs) are more commonly referred to generically as 'dioxins'. You have already met this family of chemicals in Block 0: *Chemistry* and in Block 1, but their basic structures are shown in Figure 19.

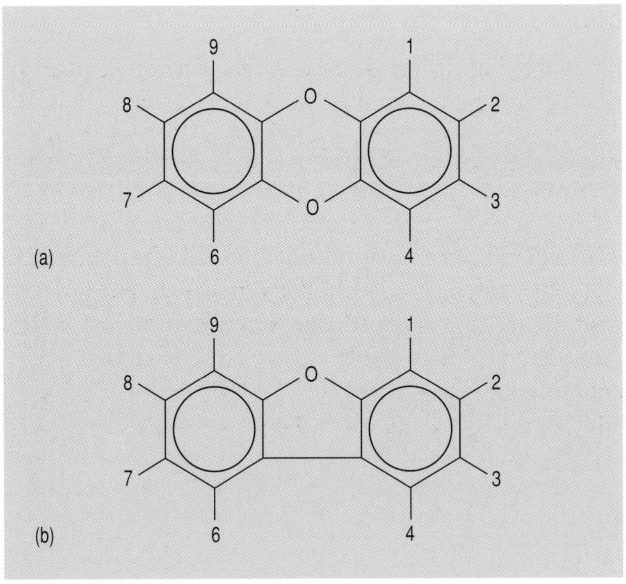

Figure 19   (a) Dioxin and (b) furan structures

Dioxins are carbon-based organic compounds which are the product of incomplete combustion. They are of particular concern in MSW incineration because of their toxicity and they are thought to be formed by several complex mechanisms in combustion systems, particularly in the post-combustion zone at temperatures of 250–350 °C. Although much research has been carried out on this subject, dioxin formation in incinerators is not completely understood.

Dioxins are controlled by primary measures, which attempt to limit the formation of dioxins, or by secondary measures which are employed to reduce dioxins once they have formed.

Primary measures include maintaining good combustion by controlling the feed rate, temperature, combustion air and mixing within the incinerator. Good combustion results in minimizing carry-over of organic material, which is a source of dioxin formation. Dioxin formation can also be minimized by avoiding the critical temperature (450 °C down to 200 °C) following combustion. Further opportunity for dioxin formation can be avoided by reducing particulate matter carry-over. Carry-over can be minimized by reducing excess air levels. Frequent cleaning of boiler tubes is also helpful.

Secondary methods that are commonly used are carbon adsorption and catalytic oxidation. With carbon adsorption, activated carbon is injected into the flue gas. This enables dioxins to be adsorbed into the carbon (along with mercury). Catalytic oxidation is a technique that destroys dioxins, converting them into CO_2, HCl and water. This reaction is often achieved by oversizing the SCR reactor used to reduce NO_x emissions.

The question of dioxin emissions from incinerators is a contentious one, so it is useful to put these emissions into context. In 1999 the UK released a total of 345 g of dioxin to the atmosphere, of which 2 g (less than 1%) was from MSW incineration (Defra, 2002). This gives an idea of the scale of the problem. However, the fact that a relatively small percentage of the total dioxin released is from incineration should not be an argument for relaxing emission standards. Rather, all industrial sectors should be working towards reducing their dioxin emissions.

9.5.6 Flue gas treatment in the UK

UK incinerators tend to use either dry or semi-dry lime injection systems followed by bag filters. Activated carbon injection is usually carried out to reduce mercury and dioxin emissions. These systems meet the emission standards required by the Environment Agency and do not generate a liquid effluent stream.

NO_x control is beginning to be installed in a number of UK incinerators. The introduction of flue gas recirculation at the Coventry incineration plant (Burnley and Aplin, 1999) has reduced NO_x emissions from around 450 mg m^{-3} to between 300 and 350 mg m^{-3}. Other plants are considering the installation of SNCR reduction to guarantee lower levels, and SNCR or SCR will be required in all new plants to meet the emission standards specified in Table 16 (page 61).

9.6 Residues from incineration

The wastes from incinerators, in the form of ash and other residues, need to be disposed of. Bottom ash accounts for about 30% by mass or 10% by volume of the input to the incinerator. The final residues from the gas scrubbing system comprise about 20–50 kg per tonne of waste burned.

After leaving the quench tank, the bottom ash is passed under an electromagnet to remove ferrous metals for recycling. The ash can then be further treated to remove non-ferrous metals using an eddy current separator (described in Section 11.5.3) and by storage for a number of months to allow the material to stabilize. At this point the ash can be recycled as a substitute for natural aggregates in road building and other construction projects. This practice happens in many mainland European countries. The combination of the landfill tax and *aggregate tax* is starting to encourage a greater use of bottom ash recycling in the UK.

Residues from the pollution abatement plant contain irritant unreacted lime, soluble chlorides and sulphates, and elevated levels of heavy metals and dioxins. A number of research groups are developing methods to reduce the dioxin content and other potential environmental problems associated with the metals and salts. At present these wastes have to be disposed of in hazardous waste landfills where they have to be isolated from the environment for the foreseeable future. However, these residues are unlikely to meet future stringent acceptance criteria for landfill, the main problem being the highly mobile chlorides. Therefore, alternative treatment/disposal routes are being sought.

9.7 Summary

Incineration with energy recovery is a well-established technology used throughout the developed world. Incineration can be effectively combined with recycling schemes with no detriment to either process and can achieve at least a 90% reduction in the volume of material sent to landfill. Many of the countries with the highest recycling rates also rely heavily on incineration.

In the UK there are 19 operational plants with several other schemes either under construction or at the development/planning stage.

Incineration is highly regulated under integrated pollution prevention and control (IPPC). Plant operators must demonstrate that their process represents the best available techniques (BAT) and extremely stringent emission standards must be met.

Most incinerators are based on grate systems, but there are also a number of fluidized bed plants in operation. Advanced thermal systems based on pyrolysis or gasification are being developed. These processes have some potential advantages over conventional incinerators, but cannot yet be classed as tried-and-tested technology.

All incinerators are fitted with gas cleaning equipment to reduce the emissions of particulate material, heavy metals, acid gases and dioxins.

Incinerators produce residues for treatment/disposal. The grate or bottom ash is usually treated to remove ferrous metal for recycling and sometimes non-ferrous metals are also recovered. The remaining material can either be landfilled as an industrial waste or recycled as an aggregate substitute. The residue from the pollution abatement plant contains elevated levels of unreacted lime, soluble salts, heavy metals and dioxins. This residue has to be disposed of as a hazardous waste.

Incineration overcomes many of the problems of landfills. Energy recovery is maximized and a certain amount of materials recovery also takes place. About half of the energy produced by incineration is derived from paper and other plant-derived material, so this proportion of the energy can be considered to be sustainably produced and have no impact on global warming. However, incineration does produce some hazardous waste which requires long-term isolation from the environment. Therefore, this aspect of incineration cannot be regarded as sustainable at present.

10 ANAEROBIC DIGESTION

10.1 Introduction

Anaerobic digestion (AD) is a bacterial process in which organic material is fermented in anaerobic (oxygen-free) conditions to produce 'biogas' – a mixture of methane and carbon dioxide and a stabilized residue known as 'digestate'. AD is a natural process that takes place in swamps, peat bogs and in the intestines of ruminants such as cows.

The process of AD was recognized as early as the 17th century, but its first practical use to treat a waste was in 1895 when sewage was digested and the gas used to light street lamps in Exeter. AD is now widely used to treat sewage sludge and this process is discussed in Chapter 10 of Block 3: *Water pollution control*. In recent years, the industry has started to adapt the technology for use with other organic wastes including organic industrial wastes (food processing for example) and source-segregated or mechanically separated MSW.

AD occupies an ambiguous position in the waste management hierarchy. It can be regarded as a 'recovery' option producing a gaseous fuel which is burned with energy recovery. On the other hand, if the feedstock is uncontaminated source-separated material and a beneficial use can be found for the digestate, AD can reasonably be classified as a 'recycling' option in the way that composting is.

AD can take place under a wide range of temperatures (10 °C to over 100 °C) and moisture levels. So-called high-solids digestion requires about 70% moisture, while at the other extreme, low-solids digestion can operate at up to 99% moisture. This means that a wide range of wastes can be treated – from MSW to diluted industrial effluents. Having said this, any particular digestion system (or digester) must be designed to treat a specific waste stream and operate under a relatively narrow range of temperature and moisture conditions.

Digesters designed to process MSW tend to be operated at temperatures above 50 °C. Providing that the processing time is long enough this temperature ensures that the digestate is sterilized and free from pathogens.

SAQ 18

Using the compositional information from SAQ 6 and your knowledge of landfill processes, estimate the proportion of household waste that could be treated by AD.

10.2 AD chemistry and biology

An anaerobic digester can be considered to be like a tightly controlled landfill reactor. Not surprisingly then, the chemical and biological processes are similar to those discussed in Section 8.1. There is, of course, one important difference: the initial aerobic stage does not occur and any aerobic treatment of the final digestate produced takes place outside the AD reactor.

The detailed chemistry and biology will not be repeated here, but this brief summary should remind you of the key points of the three-stage process of AD.

Phase 1: Hydrolysis and fermentation

In this stage, the complex organic polymers are broken down into simpler compounds. In particular, enzymes produced by bacteria break down cellulose and lipids into simple sugars and fatty acids, and proteins are broken down to simpler amino acids. Some of these amino acids are incorporated into the growing mass of bacteria while others are further degraded to ammonia and fatty acids (such as acetic acid).

The gas produced during this phase typically contains 80% carbon dioxide and 20% hydrogen.

Phase 2: Acetogenesis

In the second phase of decomposition, acetogenic bacteria convert the simple sugars into organic acids such as acetic acid (the simplest organic acid) and carbon dioxide. At the same time other bacterial communities convert more complex carbohydrates directly into acetic acid.

Phase 3: Methanogenesis

In this third stage, methane-generating bacteria (methanogens) become more active and generate methane and carbon dioxide from the acetic acid. At the same time, carbon dioxide and hydrogen (generated during the hydrolysis of lipids) are combined by other methanogenic bacteria to generate additional methane. The final gaseous product contains about 66% methane and 33% carbon dioxide.

In many ways, this phase can be considered to be the most critical. Methanogenesis only develops under a narrow range of conditions so AD systems often fail due to their inability to establish these conditions and to convert the fatty acids into methane.

10.3   Practical applications of anaerobic digestion of wastes

The most common use of AD is in treating farm wastes. In India and China six to eight million family-sized AD units are used to provide biogas for cooking and lighting. In Europe and the USA, there are over 800 farm-based systems used to treat animal slurry and other organic farm wastes. Globally, over 1000 AD plants are used to treat industrial wastes and several thousand sewage treatment works use AD to process effluents and sludges.

In 1997, the International Energy Agency's (IEA) Anaerobic Digestion Activity estimated that there were about 50 AD plants treating source-segregated MSW (often along with other organic wastes) and about 14 further plants under construction (Resource Developments Association, 1997). In addition, the IEA group identified some 55 plants processing mechanically separated MSW, industrial waste and farm wastes.

Most of these plants are in Denmark and Germany. At present (early 2007) there are no full scale plants in the UK, but two demonstration plants are undergoing trials and several larger schemes are proposed.

10.3.1   AD technology

Feed pre-processing

Many components of MSW are not amenable to digestion so some form of pre-processing is required. This may be achieved by organizing the separate collection of digestible material from households, civic amenity sites and industrial producers of large amounts of digestible wastes (food processors for example). We will be looking at the separate collections for household waste in Section 11.5.

Alternatively, mixed waste can be processed to remove most of the non-digestible material in a system similar to that used to prepare waste for fluidized bed combustion as shown in Figure 16. Mechanical processing is often cheaper than separate collection and does not rely on the active participation of the householders. On the other hand, the digestate will contain physical (small pieces of glass, plastic and metal) and chemical (heavy metals) contaminants and may have to be disposed of to landfill.

The digester

The digestion process begins with the mixing of the feedstock with water. In low-solids digestion the solids concentration is 15% or lower, while high-solids digestion operates with a solids content of around 30%. The slurry is fed into a reactor which is stirred continuously to ensure good mixing. As material is added to the reactor an equivalent volume of material is removed. As the gas forms it collects at the top of the reactor and is withdrawn into a storage vessel. The gas is usually burned on-site in a gas engine to generate power.

The digester is designed to retain material in the reactor for a period of two to four weeks and the material is heated to maintain the optimum temperature. This heating can be achieved by recovering waste heat from the exhaust gas of the engine used to burn the gas.

A typical system is shown in Figure 20.

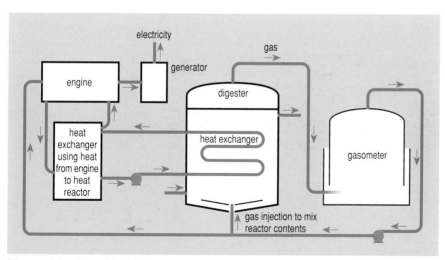

Figure 20   Simplified layout of an AD system

EXERCISE

An AD reactor is fed with 15 m^3 per day of MSW/water slurry. What does the volume of the reactor have to be if a retention time of 21 days is required?

ANSWER

The retention time (RT) has units of days (d), the volume (V) m^3 and the feed rate (F) m^3 d^{-1}. Inspection of these units shows that

$$RT = \frac{V}{F} \text{ or } V = RT \times F$$

Using the values supplied

$$V = 21 \times 15 = 315 \text{ m}^3$$

Low-solids digesters tend to give higher gas yields, but require larger reactors and a higher heating requirement than high-solids digesters with an equivalent throughput.

Digestate treatment

When digestion is complete, the digestate requires further treatment before use or disposal. Initially the excess water is removed from the solid product and returned to the process. The remaining solid is then 'cured' in an aerobic process similar to the composting processes discussed in Section 11.6. The cured product can then be used in the same way as composts. This is discussed fully in Chapter 11, but the higher quality products can be used as soil improvers or in growing media, and lower quality products can be used as landfill cover material and in landfill restoration.

10.4   Summary

Anaerobic digestion (AD) uses the biological processes taking place in landfill sites, but under controlled conditions in reactors. This process generates gas which can be used for power and/or heat generation and a digestate that can be used as a soil conditioner.

In theory, AD can treat about half of the MSW stream. The digestible waste must either be collected separately from the rest of the waste or be separated by mechanical processing before digestion. The digestate from the latter is not usually suitable for use in agricultural applications.

Globally there are around 50 plants treating source-segregated municipal wastes by AD. None of these are in the UK, but several local authorities are considering its use.

AD is a sustainable way of managing organic waste. The energy that is produced does not contribute to global warming and, providing the waste is collected separately, the digestate can be used to beneficial purpose. AD does not lead to any long-term problems or liabilities. However, it does not present a total solution; it must only be seen as a part solution to the problem of wastes.

11 RECYCLING AND COMPOSTING OF WASTES

11.1 Introduction

In the previous sections, we have looked at some of the real and perceived problems and benefits of landfill, incineration and AD. The removal of components from the waste stream for reprocessing into new materials or compost should reduce the amount of waste that remains for treatment by the above processes. In addition, the UK parliaments and assemblies have set local authorities ambitious targets for recycling materials.

In this chapter, we will look at the advantages, limitations and problems associated with waste recycling and composting, and consider the technologies involved in these operations.

Recycling can be defined as the collection of waste materials and reprocessing to provide raw materials which are then incorporated into new products. It is important to note that the process of recycling involves all of these stages. When I put bottles, cans and papers out for collection by my local authority I am only starting the recycling process. The materials are not recycled until they are incorporated into new bottles, cans, paper products and similar goods.

The collection and processing of wastes to make new materials – usually referred to as recycling – is one of the more public faces of waste management and is often seen as 'the only solution' to the waste problem. Although materials recycling is very popular with the public and well-publicized by environmental pressure groups, recycling does not present a total solution. In this chapter we will look at how much household waste is recyclable, how it can be collected and at the markets and values of the reclaimed materials.

11.2 Why recycle waste?

There are many possible answers to the question 'why recycle waste?' The results from a survey carried out in 2000 of 1000 members of the public gave a number of reasons as can be seen in Figure 21.

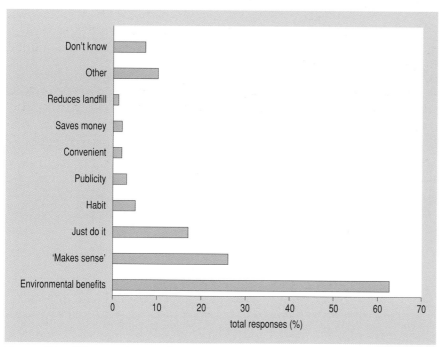

Figure 21 Why people recycle wastes (source: Burnley and Parfitt, 2000)

Local authorities and the business community will share some of these reasons but will also have other reasons for setting up or taking part in recycling schemes. Some of the main ones are discussed in the following paragraphs.

Legislation

Local authorities and some sectors of the business community are obliged to recycle specified amounts or proportions of various types of waste. Consult the Legislation Supplement for details of the current position on this, but in particular you should be aware of:

- statutory recycling rates for local authorities in England introduced as part of the implementation of the national waste strategy;

- recycling targets for the packaging industry (packaging manufacturers, packaging users and retailers) introduced under the producer responsibility regulations;

- the extension of producer responsibility to cover scrap vehicles, and electrical and electronic equipment.

Public relations

Recycling waste is a high-profile activity and is generally perceived by the public to be a 'good thing'. Local authorities and businesses can gain good publicity by being seen to be involved in recycling.

Cost savings

It is an unfortunate fact of waste management that the cost of collecting materials from household waste for recycling is nearly always more than the price paid for the material by the reprocessing industry. On the other hand, businesses that produce significant amounts of homogeneous and uncontaminated usable wastes can save on the disposal costs and landfill tax while possibly generating a small income stream.

Environmental benefits

Lastly, there can be environmental benefits associated with recycling, as over 60% of the people questioned in the above survey pointed out. These benefits must be evaluated carefully while taking account of the environmental disbenefits associated with collecting, processing and transporting the wastes. According to McDougall and White (2001):

- making newsprint from recycled fibre uses 30% less energy than newsprint manufactured from virgin wood;

- a 10% increase in the amount of waste glass (*cullet*) added to a glass-making furnace reduces energy consumption by 2.5%, particulate material emissions by 8%, NO_x emissions by 4% and SO_x emissions by 10%;

- every tonne of steel produced from scrap steel saves 1.5 tonnes of iron ore and 0.5 tonnes of coal, as well as reducing water and limestone use;

- making aluminium from scrap cans achieves a 95% saving in energy use in comparison with aluminium production from bauxite.

11.3   How much waste is recycled?

You will often see tables that compare the municipal recycling rates achieved in the UK with those of other countries (for example, Table 14 in Section 9.2 shows such a list). However, as we saw in Chapter 3 MSW only accounts for a small proportion of the total controlled waste production. If we also consider the recycling of commercial and industrial waste a different picture appears. Table 17 provides some figures for the UK. From this we could argue that England recycles 43% of its waste.

Table 17 Waste recycling in the UK

Type of waste	Amount produced (million tonnes)	Proportion recycled (%)
Commercial	41	42
Industrial	45	42
Municipal	35	25
Construction and demolition	91	50
Total	229	43

SAQ 19

Use the data in Table 17 to calculate England's municipal waste recycling and recovery rate if we were to redefine 'municipal waste' as all household and commercial waste. As you do so, keep in mind the phrase, 'There are three kinds of lies: lies, damned lies and statistics.' (Block 0: *Mathematics and statistics*, Chapter 5).

11.4 How much waste can be recycled?

The proportion of household waste that can be recycled is hotly debated. It depends on many factors including the composition of the household waste, the existence of local markets for reclaimed materials and the amount that the authority is willing to pay to recycle a given material (given the other calls on its funds such as education and health). Figures produced by the former Warren Spring Laboratory (a government-funded research organization) estimated that about 30% of the material in household waste could be recycled into new materials. In addition, organic waste composting could achieve a recycling rate of about 16%. This gives a total potential recycling rate of around 46%.

In contrast, Waste Watch (a non-governmental organization that exists to promote waste reduction, reuse and recycling) suggests that 50% of the waste can be recycled into materials and 20% composted, giving an overall potential recycling rate of 70%.

Don't be downhearted by the wide range of figures quoted when it comes to waste. Waste is an inherently variable material and (as you have already learned from your home experiment waste survey) not the most pleasant substance in the world to work with, so reliable data are scarce. To this position we can add the bias introduced by vested interests making assumptions to suit their cases, and wide variations in published figures can be expected. Now is a good time to investigate this by working through SAQ 20.

SAQ 20

Using the figures for the composition of MSW that you calculated in SAQ 6 and the following figures for recyclability of each component, calculate the maximum theoretical recycling rate for MSW and the quantity of recyclable material produced each year by a typical household. For this example, you should assume that 'recycling' covers both the recovery of materials and compost, but not energy recovery, and that the average household produces 1150 kg of waste per year.

Component	% recyclable
Paper and card	90
Dense plastic	30
Glass	95
Ferrous metal	70
Non-ferrous metal	30
Kitchen/garden waste	80

Assume that the other components are not recyclable.

The calculation in SAQ 20 gives us another figure for the recyclability of waste. If we were to change our estimate of the composition of household waste or the assumptions we make about the proportions that can be recycled this figure would change yet again. For example, market limitations mean that, in many parts of the UK, the fraction of paper that can be recycled is much smaller than 90%.

Another important fact to note is that all these figures represent maximum values and ignore the inherent inefficiencies that arise when householders are asked to become involved in the sometimes unpleasant and even insanitary business of collecting materials for recycling and composting. This problem is addressed below.

It is also important to consider how much of our commercial and industrial waste can be recycled. Some wastes that are either generated or collected separately, and so tend not to be contaminated, achieve very high recycling rates. For example, 86% of the stream identified as 'metals and scrap equipment' is recycled and 76% of the paper and card stream. Unfortunately, about half our industrial and commercial waste is classified as 'general industrial and commercial waste' and this stream achieves a much lower recycling rate of about 15%. As I have mentioned in Section 4.2, little is known about the composition of this stream and, until the material is better characterized and higher levels of segregation are achieved, significantly higher recycling rates will be difficult to achieve.

11.5   Collection of recyclable materials

The collection of materials for recycling from industrial and commercial premises is a part of the day-to-day operation of a business. Materials are usually produced in a relatively uncontaminated form in large quantities. These can be stored until a sufficient quantity accumulates to enable it to be transported directly to the reprocessor. Also, there is often a direct financial incentive for a business to reduce its waste disposal costs (or even derive income from the segregation and diversion of material from its waste stream).

In contrast, collecting materials from household waste is not a simple activity. As you found out in SAQ 20, the average household produces a maximum of about 600 kg of recyclable waste per year and around a third of this is wet (and potentially unpleasant and odorous) organic waste.

To this we must add the fact that the waste is produced in some 25 million households and that there is no financial carrot or statutory stick to make householders participate in recycling activities. However, some local authorities are considering introducing a system of fines for householders who persistently refuse to participate in kerbside recycling schemes.

In spite of this, around 80% of the population claims to recycle materials at least once a month. The number of people who recycle, and in most cases the amount of waste contributed, would increase if recycling were made easier.

11.5.1 Bring schemes

Bring (or drop-off) recycling schemes use the bottle, can and paper banks that you are probably familiar with. These sites are located at strategically placed locations such as public car parks, supermarket car parks and civic amenity waste sites. Civic amenity sites are particularly important in the collection of green waste for composting.

People bring their wastes to these sites (preferably as part of some other activity so a special journey is not made by car) and when the banks are full they are collected and taken to a materials recovery facility for bulking and transport to the reprocessors. All local authorities use bring systems to some extent.

Bring recycling systems are cheaper to operate than kerbside collection schemes, but achieve a much lower recovery rate. The Department of Trade and Industry estimates that a well-operated network of bring sites (with one site per 750–1000 people) can achieve a recovery rate of 6–10%.

11.5.2 Kerbside schemes

In a kerbside collection scheme each participating household is given one or more containers to store recyclable wastes which are then collected by, or on behalf of, the local authority. In some authorities the collection vehicle crew sorts the materials at the kerbside and places them in different compartments on the vehicle. Other authorities simply collect the mixed recyclable materials for sorting at the materials recovery facility.

Schemes range from the very simple, where only newspapers are collected, to complex, where different materials are collected in different weeks. For example, in parts of south Northamptonshire the council provides each household with a green wheeled bin for organic waste and two plastic boxes; one for paper, glass and textiles and one for plastic and metal cans. A black wheeled bin is used for the residual waste. On one week the green wheeled bin and the first recycling box are collected and in the other week the black wheeled bin and the second recycling box are collected. Householders are given a calendar to remind them which bins to put out on which dates and information sheets are also circulated to remind people of the materials that can be recycled.

Schemes such as this can be effective in collecting up to 40% of household waste for materials recycling and composting (discussed in Section 11.6). The reduction in frequency of the residual waste collection from a weekly to a fortnightly service also encourages householders to think about waste minimization. However, such schemes are expensive to operate – needing two collections from each household per week – and require a high degree of cooperation from the residents. For both these reasons, such schemes tend to be most effective in prosperous areas such as small towns and the more wealthy areas of cities.

The number of kerbside schemes has grown rapidly in recent years and in 2003/04 coverage had reached 80% of households in England. By 2010 this figure will be close to 100%.

Note that I have not yet considered the cost of collecting or processing wastes and this is discussed in Chapter 13.

11.5.3   Processing collected materials

Once materials have been collected from the business premises, kerbside or bring site, further processing is necessary before the materials can be transported to the reprocessor. Where the wastes are collected in a segregated form or sorted by the collection crew, all that is required is to bulk the material into loads that can be transported at a reasonable cost. At the other extreme, where mixed recyclable wastes are collected, there is a need for complex separation equipment. In either case this processing is carried out at a plant known as a *materials recovery facility* or MRF (often referred to as a 'murf').

Examples of simple and complex MRFs are shown in Figures 22 and 23.

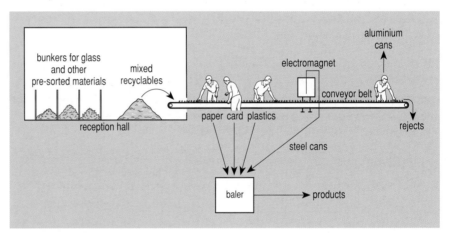

Figure 22   Simple MRF

The simple MRF

Simple MRFs tend to use hand sorting when required and don't rely on mechanical sorting techniques. If the MRF is handling mixed recyclables, the materials are transferred from the reception area to a conveyor that runs past a sorting platform. Operators standing by the conveyor pick out specified materials and throw them down chutes into storage containers. Electromagnets are often mounted above the conveyor to separate out ferrous metal cans.

Any material reaching the end of the conveyor is either too small to separate out by hand or consists of material that should not have been included with the recyclables. This reject stream is also directed down a chute for eventual transfer to landfill or incineration. Rejects can account for 15% or even more of the input mass to the MRF.

The sorting platform is often enclosed in a cabin to reduce exposure to noise from balers, vehicles, etc. The cabin may also be air-conditioned to make conditions more comfortable.

The separated products are either taken directly to merchants for further processing or, in the case of paper, plastics and cans, passed through a baler to increase the density and hence the vehicle payload.

Simple MRFs that process material which has already been separated by the collection vehicle crew require even less equipment. A series of

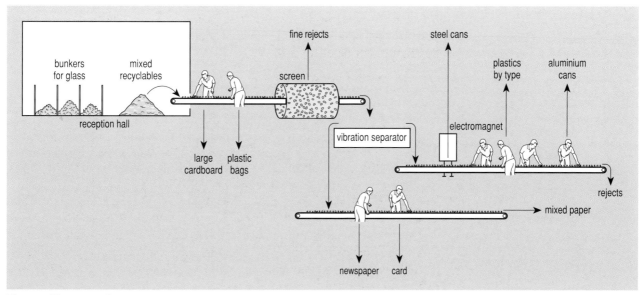

Figure 23 Complex MRF

storage bays, a baler and an electromagnet to separate ferrous and non-ferrous cans may be all that is necessary.

SAQ 21

Use the information in the table below, and the results of SAQ 6, to calculate the household waste recycling rate if the whole UK were to adopt a scheme to collect paper, dense plastic, glass, metals and compostable waste from households. Assume that:

■ the percentage of households participating in any given week is 75%;

■ the percentage of material rejected by the MRF or compost plant is 5%.

Material	Proportion of material that is theoretically recyclable (%)	Proportion of material that householders put out for recycling (%)
Paper and card	90	90
Dense plastic	30	50
Glass	95	80
Ferrous metal	70	50
Non-ferrous metal	30	70
Compostable waste	80	70

If the figures that we used in this calculation are correct, the UK will fall short of the national recycling targets (50% in the long term). Of course, it may be that I am being pessimistic about the likely participation in recycling by householders and maybe more people will be willing to rinse out their food cans than I predicted. However, it is clear that real recycling rates are likely to be much lower than the theoretical value of 53% we estimated in SAQ 20.

The complex MRF

In the more complex MRFs, mixed recyclable materials (paper, plastics and metals, but not glass) are tipped into a reception area where large cardboard items, carrier bags and unwanted materials are removed by hand. The remaining waste is then carried by conveyor belt to a screen where particles less than 50 mm in size are removed as rejects and sent for landfill or incineration. The larger material passes on to a vibrating belt where the bouncing action separates plastic bottles and cans from flatter items such as paper. The bottles and cans roll onto a separate conveyor which passes under a magnetic separator that removes ferrous metal cans for baling. The aluminium cans and plastics then pass a picking station where the cans and various grades of plastic are sorted by hand.

The paper that remains on the vibrating belt is also sorted by hand into two categories before baling: newspapers and magazines, and mixed paper.

Other equipment that can be used in complex MRFs to reduce the need for people to come into contact with the waste includes:

■ bag splitters, for use where the mixed recyclable materials are collected in one-trip plastic bags;

■ air classifiers, where the feed is passed through an air stream which entrains lighter materials such as paper and plastics;

■ eddy-current separators, a system of opposing magnetic forces directed on a conveyor that cause non-ferrous metals to be ejected at right angles to the direction of travel of the conveyor;

■ optical sorting devices to identify specific materials on a conveyor that can then be blown off by air jets, rams or robotic arms (also used to separate different grades of plastics from mixed plastic streams).

As is the case with simple MRFs, around 10–15% of the material entering a complex MRF is not suitable for recycling and forms the reject stream. You should also note that in areas served by this type of recycling scheme glass is collected separately through bring sites. Glass is not processed in this type of MRF because it leads to high levels of contamination of the other products and unacceptable risks to the operators due to breakages.

Note that in both types of MRF people are employed to hand sort a waste-derived material. The operators will frequently come into contact with broken glass and sharp edges on cans. Although the material should not be contaminated operators may also encounter used nappies, animal faeces and syringes. Some plants employ people with learning difficulties as operators and argue that it provides work in a sheltered environment for people who would otherwise be unemployable. On the other hand, some consider that this practice exploits the disadvantaged in forcing them to do work that more able people would refuse to do. The educational benefits of such work are also debatable.

Regardless of the amount of hand sorting that is carried out, the operation of an MRF can generate high levels of noise, dust and bioaerosols. Bioaerosols consist of bacteria, fungi and cell wall components, and can cause infection and allergic reactions in exposed people (particularly those with a history of asthma or eczema). This problem was studied by researchers working on behalf of the Environment Agency who confirmed that, in some MRFs, operators are exposed to unacceptable levels of these pollutants (Gladding, undated).

SAQ 22

Draw up a table listing all the potential public health and environmental impacts of the operation of an MRF, and ways that these impacts could be minimized.

SAQ 23

You met Sankey diagrams in Block 0: *Mathematics and statistics*. Refer back to that block and then use the information from SAQ 21 to produce a Sankey diagram that illustrates the material flows when recycling paper from household waste.

11.5.4 Recovery of materials from mixed waste

It is theoretically possible to use the technology described above for the complex MRF to recover materials for recycling from a mixed waste stream. Such a plant could recover paper, metals, plastics, organic material for composting and even glass. However, these products would be highly contaminated through contact with food waste, liquids and pathogens (in nappies, cat litter, etc.) and have little, if any, potential uses or value.

From time to time experiments are carried out to process mixed waste for recycling, but high reject rates and lack of markets for the contaminated products meant that in early 2002 there were few, if any, large-scale plants in operation in the UK.

11.6 Waste composting

11.6.1 Introduction – what is compost?

You are probably familiar with terms such as 'potting compost' and 'seed compost' seen on labels in garden centres. You need to take care with these labels. Some of this material may well contain compost in the correct sense of the word, but much of it (such as peat-based products) is not compost. The lay-person can be forgiven for misusing the term compost, but we have to be a little more strict. Compost is correctly defined as:

> ... the stable material produced by the aerobic biological decomposition of organic wastes under controlled conditions.

When we are discussing composting as a recycling activity we must remember that a material is not considered to be recycled until it is incorporated into a usable product. So we need to add the following to our definition:

> ... the compost produced must be suitable for use in a soil conditioner or growing medium.

Composting processes

When you read the heading 'waste composting' you may have started to think about making compost from garden and kitchen waste at home in a compost heap or bin. On the other hand, particularly if your local authority collects waste for composting, you may have a mental picture of a series of two metre high piles of wastes several tens of metres in length. Both pictures are equally correct. In the UK, about one-third of all households make compost in their gardens and there are 150 large-scale composting processes in operation. From the waste management point of view, both processes have their advantages.

Home composting is a cheap option for a local authority. Even if the authority gives compost bins to householders, this is a one-off cost. The costs associated with collecting waste every one or two weeks are eliminated, as are the processing costs. The environmental impacts of collection (noise, traffic, exhaust fumes) and processing (odours, visual impact, noise) are also avoided. Finally, the active participation of the householders means that people are thinking more about the waste they generate and how it is disposed of. Thinking back to the waste hierarchy in Chapter 1, home composting can be regarded as a form of waste reuse or even waste reduction.

Centralized composting is an effective way of recycling organic waste from public parks and gardens so, if a centralized composting plant is built to treat this material, it may as well also take household organic waste. Composting is carried out under tightly controlled conditions and with a mix of feedstocks so the final product will be superior to that of most home compost bins. Centralized composting requires less effort on the householder's part than home composting, so participation rates should be higher. Finally, centralized composting counts towards a local authority's recycling rate calculations, unlike home composting. So by accepting household organic waste a local authority increases its chances of meeting its statutory recycling targets.

11.6.2   Uses of compost

In our definition of compost, I said that the compost had to be suitable for use in a growing medium or soil conditioner. This means that the compost must have a beneficial effect on the plants and/or soil it is used with and have acceptably low levels of biological, chemical and physical contaminants.

This definition raises several important points. The most significant is that, in the context of a recycling option, the compost must be usable by gardeners, growers, construction companies or farmers.

Finally, we need to consider what we mean by 'growing medium' or 'soil conditioner'. Growing media are used for planting seeds, rooting cuttings and growing plants in containers or growing bags depending on the formulation. The medium needs to have the correct levels of plant nutrients and good water-holding properties.

Soil conditioners or improvers are incorporated into soils usually to increase the levels of organic material or to improve the water-holding or drainage properties of the soil. Common soil improvers are peat, coir and used mushroom compost.

Generally speaking, composts cannot be used as growing media without modification or dilution. Common problems are:

- the pH is too high;

- the conductivity (a measure of salt content) is too high;

- there are excessive potassium concentrations;

- there is insufficient soluble nitrogen and phosphorus;

- the bulk density is too high.

Manufacturers of growing media have overcome these problems by diluting the compost with another material (coir, peat, wood fibre or bark for example) and/or by the addition of acidic materials and nutrients. Of course this adds to the cost of producing the compost, but is an essential stage if the aim is to produce a useful product for gardeners and growers.

A third use for composted waste is as a mulch. Mulches are used to provide a surface cover for soils. These help to reduce weed growth and water loss from the soil and can be decorative. Bark or wood chippings are often used as mulches and the larger size fraction of composted wastes can also be used for this purpose.

The above uses all require a reasonably high-quality product in terms of nutrient and contaminant levels. Not all compost operators aim for these standards because there are a number of low-grade uses for composts which can accept lower-specification products which tend to be cheaper to produce than the better composts.

Contaminated land

Contaminated land is discussed in Chapter 17, but at this stage all you need to be aware of is that land that has been polluted by previous industrial uses can often be lacking in the organic material necessary to build up a soil that can support a variety of plant life and a healthy population of microbes and invertebrates. Compost can be ideal material to provide this organic matter. It tends to be produced in urban areas where most of the contaminated land is found and has a lower price than alternative organic materials.

There are also advantages from the compost producer's point of view. Contaminated land uses can accept a lower grade product than horticultural or agricultural uses, so the producer does not have to ensure the removal of every small piece of plastic or metal in the compost. Also, while the price is low, contaminated land treatment could provide an output for a producer's entire output, eliminating the effort associated with finding other markets.

Landfill use

As discussed in Chapter 8, landfill sites require large volumes of material for use as daily cover material and for final restoration material above the capping layer. Composted waste can provide an ideal cover material. A very low-grade product can be made by composting the fine material screened from mixed waste. While such compost would have no use in agriculture, horticulture or even for contaminated land treatment, it would be suitable for landfill daily cover use.

It is, however, debatable whether such a use is classed as recycling. On the one hand it provides a real need and replaces alternative cover materials. On the other, the displaced material may also be a waste (rubble, for example) and use in landfill is hardly what the general public would understand by 'recycling'.

11.6.3   What can be composted?

In principle, all food waste and garden plant-based wastes (with the exception of large woody items) can be composted. In addition, a certain amount of waste paper or card can be added to this material. However, this wide range of materials ignores operator and public health concerns during processing and use of the compost. Therefore:

- no centralized composting schemes will accept dog and cat faeces and they should never be used in home composting (due to concern over toxocariasis and toxoplasmosis);

- outdoor composting schemes do not accept any meat products or cooked vegetables (to reduce flies, rats and birds) and these materials should not be composted at home;

■ Under regulations introduced following the foot and mouth disease outbreak, kitchen waste of any kind can only be composted in enclosed systems that meet specified operating conditions.

11.6.4   The biochemistry of composting

Composting is a complex process involving many groups of bacteria, fungi and protozoa. There is a high degree of interaction between the groups. For example, some micro-organisms use enzymes to degrade organic molecules that are further degraded by other organisms.

At this point you may wish to refer back to Block 0: *Biology* to revise the areas of microbial cell metabolism, growth and reproduction.

The micro-organisms responsible for the composting reactions are present in all wastes and in the air. The decomposition reactions provide energy for cell metabolism and also provide materials for cell growth and reproduction. Energy is provided by the process of respiration which consumes oxygen and organic material and releases carbon dioxide. Carbon in the waste is used to form new cell walls and membrane and protoplasm. Nitrogen is mainly consumed in the production of cell protoplasm.

The composting process itself can be summarized in the following reaction

$$\text{fresh organic waste} + O_2 \longrightarrow \text{stabilized organic residue} + CO_2 + H_2O + \text{heat}$$

This process breaks down the structure of the waste material, converting complex polymers into a stable humus material. The process also releases or mineralizes many water-soluble nutrients and trace elements which can then be reused by the growing plants.

In more detail, the large-scale composting of waste can be considered to take place in the following four stages. These stages should all occur in home composting, but tend to be less clearly defined.

Stage one
On formation of the compost pile, mesophilic organisms (those that operate best in the temperature range 25–45 °C) are dominant and rapidly break down sugars, starch and simple proteins, releasing heat. Degradation takes place rapidly and the temperature rises exponentially. The pH falls to as low as 5.0 due to the formation of organic acids. During this phase, the temperature will rise as a result of the intensive microbial action providing a sufficient mass of material is present (this is often not the case in home composting). Depending on conditions, stage one lasts from one to four days.

Stage two
Once the temperature exceeds 45 °C, the mesophilic organisms become dormant or die and thermophilic microbes (optimum temperature range 45–70 °C) become active. During this phase, the rate of waste breakdown increases and the pH rises to around 8.5. The temperature reaches the levels necessary to kill weed seeds and pathogenic micro-organisms. Under optimum process conditions this stage lasts from one to three weeks, but if conditions are sub-optimal a longer period is required. During this stage it is important to use the methods discussed in the following section to prevent the temperature exceeding about 65 °C when even thermophilic organisms start to become dormant or die.

Stage three

As nutrient and energy sources become depleted microbial activity reduces and the compost temperature begins to fall. Mesophilic organisms become active again, particularly filamentous bacteria such as actinomycetes and fungi. Degradation of the more stable components in the feedstock takes place. Lignin (present in wood) is broken down by the basidiomycete group of fungi and cellulose (present in cell walls) is degraded by actinomycetes.

Stage four

This final phase is a continuation of stage three and the break point between the two stages is often arbitrary. In this maturation or curing period the temperature slowly falls to ambient levels as microbial activity greatly decreases. It is important for process operators to ensure that this phase is completed or degradation may restart during storage or use of the product. The durations of stages three and four depend on the conditions and feedstock composition, but they generally take from 30 to 90 days to be completed.

The speed of the process is dependent on a number of factors relating to the feedstock material and the process conditions. The main factors are summarized in Table 18.

Table 18 Factors controlling the composting process

Factor	Range of levels	Comments
Feedstock carbon/ nitrogen ratio	20:1 to 25:1	Too high a ratio and degradation rates slow, too low a ratio and ammonia is released
Feedstock nutrient levels	Nutrients are usually present in sufficient levels in most compost feedstocks (but large amounts of paper sludges and other commercial wastes may lead to deficiencies)	Process requires Ca, N, P, K, Co, Mn, Mg and Cu
Particle size	50–150 mm	In general the smaller the particle size the faster the decomposition rate (because the reactions take place on the particle surfaces). However, if the particles are too small compaction can take place leading to waterlogging and anaerobic conditions
Temperature	Biological optimum 35–55 °C; maximum 65 °C (temperatures greater than the biological optimum may be required to ensure that pathogenic organisms are killed)	Above 65 °C even thermophilic microbes become inactive or die
pH	5–8.5, reaching 8.0 on completion of the process	pH control is not a problem when composting most wastes
Moisture content	40–60%	Microbial activity ceases at moisture levels below 8–12%. At levels above 60% waterlogging can be a problem leading to anaerobic conditions
Oxygen content	18%	It is important to ensure that anaerobic pockets are not allowed to form

Progression of the composting process and compost stability

It is vital that the final compost produced is stable and will not continue to decompose on storage or use. There are several tests for compost stability, but one way is to look at the rate of change of the amount of carbon present in the composting waste.

At this point, if you are not confident with the term 'rate of change' please refer back to Block 0: *Mathematics and statistics* for an introduction to the subject.

Figure 24 shows a graph of organic matter content against time.

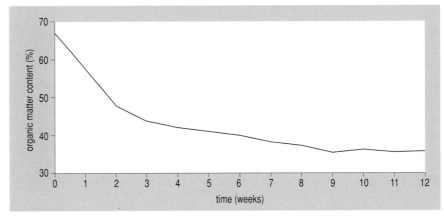

Figure 24

SAQ 24

What does the gradient (or slope) of the graph in Figure 24 tell us about the composting process during the first few weeks and what implications does this have for the process operator?

Another important reason for ensuring that the compost is fully stable is that immature compost can be detrimental to soils and any plants growing there. During the first stage of composting, organic acids are formed (especially if anaerobic conditions are allowed to develop). These acids are phytotoxic (toxic to plants) and can inhibit seed germination and plant growth. Seed germination and plant growth can also be inhibited by many other chemical factors such as high levels of ammonia (found in some immature composts) and excessively high nutrient levels often associated with composts derived from municipal botanical or green wastes. Very high levels of nutrients or salts will often inhibit germination and initial plant growth through a reduction in the ability to absorb water.

There are several ways of evaluating the chemical characteristics and phytotoxicity of partially composted wastes and composts, but one of the simplest ways is to test the effect of this material on growing plants. This is known as a *bioassay* and you will undertake a simple bioassay using cress during the second of your home experiments for this block. In fact, now is a good time to do the cress experiment. You will be investigating the effect of possible phytotoxicity and high compost nutrient levels on the development of cress seeds by testing a sample of home compost or municipal compost. You will do this by extracting the water-soluble material from the compost sample, making a number of dilutions of the extract and testing what effect these solutions have on the germination and early growth of cress seeds. You will then calculate a germination index (GI) for each solution and compare them with the GI for water which acts as a control. A high GI represents high seed germination and good initial growth, which indicates that the compost is not phytotoxic and does not have an excessively high nutrient content. Conversely, a low GI would suggest that the compost is phytotoxic or the plant nutrient levels are too high.

Determining the GI at different stages of the composting process is a useful method of monitoring the progress of composting. Figure 25 shows the results of such an exercise. It can be seen that the GI typically increases over time as the partially composted waste becomes stabilized and the levels of phytotoxins, such as organic acids, diminish. High and stable values for the GI indicate that the active composting stage can be terminated and the compost maturation stage begun.

It is usual to assume that composted material with a GI greater than 60% will have little detrimental effect on plant development.

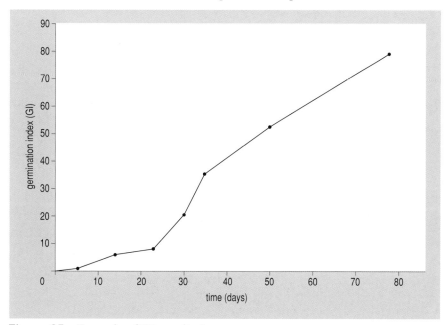

Figure 25   Example of GI monitoring

11.6.5   Composting technology

Composting plants fall into three main groups:

■   outdoor or indoor turned 'windrows';

■   outdoor or indoor aerated static piles;

■   in-vessel systems where composting takes place in an enclosed container.

Turned windrows

In windrow composting, the waste is piled into triangular cross-section heaps (the windrows). These heaps are usually about 2 m high, 3–4 m wide at the bottom and up to 50 m in length (depending on the space available). Turning is carried out for three reasons: to aerate the windrow, to avoid overheating and to mix the waste to ensure that the whole of the windrow experiences the temperature regime necessary to destroy pathogens and to complete the composting process.

Turning can be carried out using a tractor fitted with a loading shovel, but purpose-designed turners are available that straddle the windrow and use a rotating flail to mix the compost, allow good aeration and effect some particle size reduction. Figure 26 shows such a windrow turning machine. The frequency of turning depends on the activity in the pile and its temperature. In general, the most active phase of the composting process is during the first two weeks or so when most of the waste decomposition takes place (as indicated in Figure 24). Ideally, turning is required every other day during this initial phase, with the frequency dropping to weekly in stages two and three. During the maturation stage turning does not usually take place.

Figure 26 Windrow turning machine

Aerated static piles

In aerated static pile systems, the windrows are constructed over a perforated pipe connected to a fan. Air is either blown or sucked through the pile to provide aeration and to control the temperature (Figure 27). If the air is sucked through the pile the discharged air can be passed through a biofilter. In summary these consist of a mass of substrate material housing microbial communities that break down odour-forming compounds. In composting plants the substrate would normally be mature compost.

Biofilters are discussed in Block 6: Air quality management.

Unlike turned windrow systems the pile is usually not disturbed during processing. Therefore the windrow needs to be insulated to reduce heat loss and allow the surfaces to reach the required temperatures. Insulation is usually provided by a layer of mature compost, wood chippings, bracken or similar material.

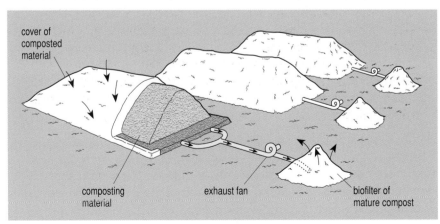

Figure 27 Aerated static pile composting system

Enclosed systems

Enclosed composting has several potential advantages over open-air systems:

- the composting material is protected from the elements;

- environmental emissions and public exposure can be more easily controlled;

- anaerobic conditions are reduced or eliminated which reduces odours;

- conditions can be controlled to provide optimum conditions for the composting micro-organisms;

- the time taken for composting to be completed is significantly lower than for open systems;

- the product has a more predictable and uniform quality and properties;

- the process can be controlled better to ensure the required temperatures are met for a sufficient time period;

- detailed records can be kept of the composting process.

These last two points are a requirement if the composted material contains any kitchen waste (including raw vegetables and peelings).

However, open-air systems are less expensive to construct, and today most UK compost plants operate in this way.

The main types of enclosed system are covered in the following paragraphs and are illustrated in Figure 28.

The simplest system is to enclose the compost windrows in an enclosed building. The material is moved through the process and turned using similar methods to conventional windrow composting. Aeration is usually achieved by either blowing or sucking air through channels in the floor beneath the windrows. Suction has the advantage that the process air can be treated in a biofilter to remove odours and dust before being discharged.

- In agitated bay systems the composting material is held in large bays around 2 m in depth. The tops of the walls dividing the bays are fitted with rails that support and guide an overhead turner. As with the enclosed building system, aeration is provided through channels in the floor.

- Containers built of wood or metal or based on the containers used in road and rail transport can be used to form modular systems that can be easily expanded or reduced to meet changes in demand. These systems can also be made in a transportable form for uses where waste arisings are seasonal. The containers operate in a very similar way to static pile systems. Waste is loaded into the container and forced aeration is applied through the floor. No turning takes place; when the process is complete the compost is removed and another batch is added.

■ In silos or towers, the feedstock is fed into the top of the tower and falls under its own weight as composted material is removed from the base of the tower. Air is blown up through the composting material from the base and can be exhausted through a biofilter. Some tower systems incorporate mixing of the composting waste by means of mechanical paddles.

■ Drum composters consist of a long drum mounted at a slight angle to the horizontal. The rotation of the drum moves the composting material from the inlet to the outlet while providing aeration. *Tunnels* operate in a similar manner, but the composting material is forced through the tunnel from the pressure of the incoming waste and aeration is provided through the floor.

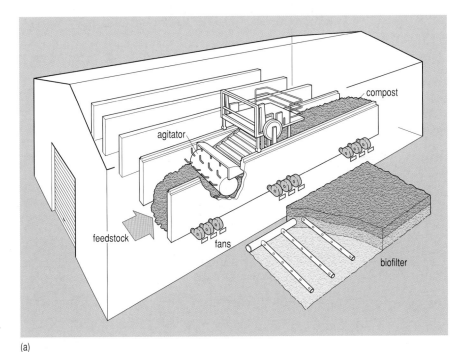

(a)

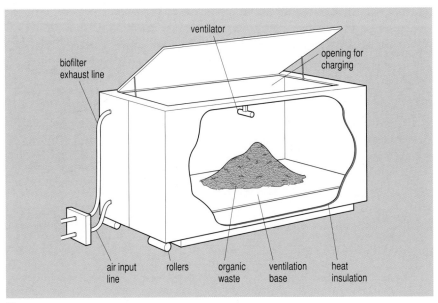

(b)

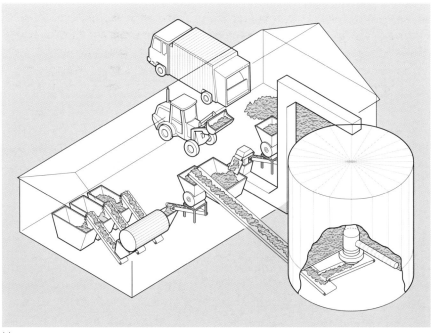

(c)

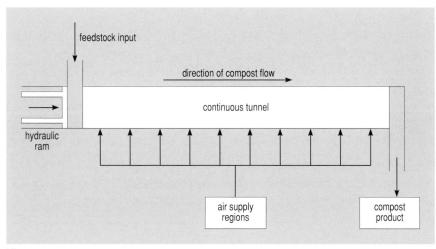

(d)

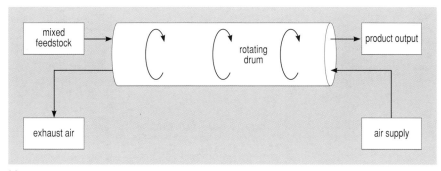

(e)

Figure 28   Enclosed composting systems: (a) agitated bays; (b) container; (c) tower system; (d) ram-fed tunnel; (e) drum schematic; (source: Border, 2003)

11.6.6   Whole waste composting

In the 1970s, some local authorities experimented with composting mixed MSW and then screening the product to separate out the 'compost' from the remaining waste. Not surprisingly the products tended to be low grade, had high heavy metal levels and were contaminated with plastic, metal and other non-compostable wastes. There was virtually no market for this compost and the experiments were abandoned.

However, this process forms a central part of mechanical biological treatment (MBT), a technique being adopted in several parts of the UK to help meet the requirements of the landfill directive. Mixed waste is subjected to a sequence of separation processes and the organic-rich fraction is composted with the aim of reducing its water and biodegradable material contents before being landfilled. Some MBT processes also recover metals for recycling and produce a paper-rich fraction that can be burned as a fuel (providing the combustion plant meets the requirements of the incineration directive and related legislation).

11.6.7   Compost standards

Composts have a variety of uses which may have a significant impact on the health of the public and on the environment. In particular, composts may be used in growing food crops and in domestic gardens where small children can come into contact with them. Therefore it is essential that composts are produced to standards which ensure that the product does not have any adverse effect on human health or the environment. Therefore a standard has been produced by the British Standards Institution (BSI 2005) known as 'PAS 100'. This standard specifies process controls, record keeping, input material selection, sanitization, stabilization and quality control requirements. The emphasis is on managing the process which requires the operators of compost sites to keep detailed records. PAS 100 also requires product identification and traceability. For full details of the requirements of PAS 100 you should consult the above reference. However, you should be aware of the following key points:

■ To comply with PAS 100, the compost must only be made from source-segregated wastes, so compost produced in MBT processes will not comply (but sewage sludge can be used as a feedstock).

■ The quality requirements listed in Table 19 must be met.

Table 19 PAS 100 quality requirements

Product criteria	Upper limit
Human pathogens	
Salmonella spp	Absent from a 25 g sample
Escherichia coli	1 000 cfu g^{-1}
Potentially toxic elements	
Cadmium	1.5 mg kg^{-1} dry matter
Chromium	100 mg kg^{-1} dry matter
Copper	200 mg kg^{-1} dry matter
Lead	200 mg kg^{-1} dry matter
Mercury	1.0 mg kg^{-1} dry matter
Nickel	50 mg kg^{-1} dry matter
Zinc	400 mg kg^{-1} dry matter
Physical contaminants	
Glass, metal, plastic and other non-stone fragments	0.5 % of air dried sample (maximum 0.25% plastics)
Stones >4 mm	8% grades other than mulch 16% mulch
Weed seeds and propagules	
Germinating weed seeds or propagule regrowth	0 per litre of compost

Note: The compost must also meet a stability test (in terms of the amount of CO_2 released when the compost is incubated under specified standard conditions) and plant growth and germination standards.

Other organizations have standards for potentially toxic element (PTE) levels in composts and similar material, and these are shown in Table 20. Table 20 also shows the levels measured in composts from three sites processing source-segregated green wastes and kitchen wastes during an Environment Agency Research project (Environment Agency, 2000). These results show that metal levels in composts cover a wide range of values and some of the higher values would not meet all of these standards.

Table 20 PTE standards and measured values in mg kg^{-1} (dry matter)

Element	Eco-label for compost	Soil Association standard for manures	Soil Association standard for soils	European Commission draft values for composts[a]	Values measured in composts
Zinc	300	1000	150	200–400	126–220
Copper	75	400	50	100–150	6–81
Nickel	50	100	50	50–75	5–64
Lead	140	250	100	100–150	<1–223
Cadmium	1.5	10	2	0.7–1.5	<0.5–10.5
Chromium	140	1000		100–150	<1–49
Mercury	1	2		0.5–1	<0.5–<1.0

[a]The European Commission values are taken from a discussion document that may become a directive following extensive review and discussion by Member States.

11.6.8   Waste composting in the UK

The Composting Association carries out an annual survey of waste composting in the UK and has reported that the UK composted 2.67 million tonnes of waste in 2004/05, which is 2.6 times the amount composted in 2000/01. The sources of the waste are summarised in Table 21.

Table 21   Wastes composted in the UK in 2004/05

Category	Quantity composted (tonnes)	Percentage of total
Household		
Garden waste from CA sites and bring schemes	1 127 000	42.2
Garden waste from kerbside collection schemes	779 000	29.2
Garden and kitchen waste from kerbside collection schemes	128 000	4.8
Kitchen waste only from kerbside collection schemes	3 000	0.1
Green waste from schools and colleges	6 000	0.2
Other household wastes	135 000	5.0
Total household	2 178 000	81.5
Municipal non-household		
Council parks and gardens waste	51 000	1.9
Other municipal non-household	12 000	0.4
Total municipal non-household	63 000	2.4
Non-municipal		
Landscape/grounds maintenance	135 000	5
Forestry/timber/bark/by-products	57 000	2.2
Food processing by-products	93 000	3.5
Food waste from shops/caterers	2 000	0.1
Paper and cardboard	2 000	0.1
Sewage sludge	7 000	0.3
Paper sludge	1 000	0.1
Manure/straw	3 000	0.1
Other	131 000	4.9
Total non-municipal waste	431 000	16.1
Total	**2 672 000**	**100**

Source: Boulos, Pocock and Gilbert (2006)

The important points to note from Table 21 are that the main sources of municipal waste for composting are the relatively clean wastes obtained from civic amenity sites and local authority parks and gardens. Together these account for 73% of MSW composting. These botanical wastes (grass, plant prunings and woody material) are collectively known as green waste and the resulting composted material is often termed green waste compost. Collection of waste from individual households in kerbside schemes accounted for about one third of MSW composting collections. This shows a rapid rise in five years from a figure of 8%. Further increases in kerbside collections are to be expected as part of the Local Authority responses to the landfill directive.

Composting is still a relatively low-technology operation. In 2004/05 some 60% of the material was processed in open windrow turned systems, but 23% was composted in in-vessel systems. This is up from 5% in 1999 and reflects both the changes in the regulations relating to the composting of kitchen waste and the difficulty in obtaining planning approval for open windrows in some locations.

Finding markets for waste composts is not an easy task. According to the Composting Association's figures, 49% of the compost was sold, but 31% was used on site by the producer and 20% was given away. The largest markets for compost were:

- Agriculture – taking 30% of the total in bulk quantities.

- Amateur horticulture – using 23% in a high value market where compost is incorporated into growing bags and soil improvers for sale to the public.

- Landscaping – another bulk market taking 17% for use in construction, road building and other landscaping projects.

The amount of waste-derived compost produced in the UK will continue to increase in the future since the development of industrial-scale composting is a key feature in the Government's strategy for fulfilling the requirements of the landfill directive. At present, the composting industry is expanding at around 25% per year and some forecasters have suggested that in order to comply with the landfill directive, the current composting capacity needs to increase at least three-fold from the 2004/05 level. As a result, it is expected that the municipal waste composting sector will need to increase its processing capacity to at least 10 million tonnes of garden and kitchen waste per year by the year 2020. Finding markets for the estimated 5 million tonnes of compost products produced will be a challenge to the industry. Agricultural applications have been identified as a major potential outlet for most of this composted material and it has been estimated that the market for compost in agriculture could be as much as 148 million tonnes per year.

Agricultural soils can benefit in at least two ways from the incorporation of compost as a soil conditioner. Firstly, soil organic matter in the UK has been declining in recent years due to intensive farming and regular applications of compost can restore the necessary physical structure to degraded soils. Secondly, waste-derived compost contains high levels of soluble nutrients and trace elements, making compost ideal for organic farming, while also helping to reduce inputs of expensive inorganic fertilizers for more intensive systems.

In addition to relatively low-value agricultural markets, higher-value markets for specialist compost products of up to 4.5 million tonnes per year have been identified in other sectors such as professional horticulture, forestry and the retail gardening market through garden centres and DIY stores.

Most of the high-value plant growing media sold in the UK contain peat rather than compost. According to government estimates around 96% of media used for growing plants, such as so-called multipurpose or potting composts, are peat-based. Peat is an acidic, fibrous material derived from the slow decomposition of vegetation over many thousands of years, and is mined from the earth and sold with relatively little additional processing. Despite the environmental damage resulting from peat extraction, peat is extensively used in plant growing media. This is mainly because it has a low pH, which plants favour, and is typically very low in nutrients, which can then be added as inorganic nutrients at a later stage to suit individual plant types. However, the Government's commitment to phase out peat extraction in the UK is likely to create a significant market for quality waste-derived composts through the gradual substitution of green waste compost into specialist and high-value peat-based products. For example, English Nature and the Royal Society for the Protection of Birds (RSPB) have estimated that by 2007, the amount of green waste compost that will be needed just to replace the partial reduction in the use of peat will be about 1 million tonnes per year. This is approximately twice the total UK production of green waste compost in 1999.

Clearly, significant markets for compost already exist and growing environmental awareness is creating more attractive, higher-value markets for green waste composts as peat substitutes. Green waste composts will also have to compete with the growing production of commercial composts derived from non-municipal sources such as industrial wood processing residues. For example, forest bark residue, when processed and composted, becomes a very fibrous material, which can have similar properties to peat. It is a feature of composts derived from green or botanical wastes that they tend to be alkaline and contain excessive and unbalanced levels of soluble nutrients. In high specification growing media it is not possible to use unmodified green composts as a direct replacement for peat. However, current research suggests that green waste composts can be amended to reduce the pH. Careful blending of green waste composts with composted wood residues and their gradual introduction into peat-based media could lead to increased penetration of the specialist growing media market.

If the industrial-scale composting sector is to expand and play a role in diverting significant amounts of municipal biodegradable waste from landfill, it will be necessary to establish wider and higher value markets for waste-derived composts. To enable this to happen, it is clear that we need to increase our understanding of the relationship between the characteristics of waste-derived composts and the precise requirements of plants and soils.

11.7   Summary

Recycling materials or compost from waste is an effective way of reducing the need for landfill and conserving resources. England recycles around 42% of its industrial and commercial wastes. Recycling is also popular with the public, and household waste recycling rates are currently above 25%. The impact of the national waste strategies and the landfill directive will result in a significant increase in this figure in the period up to 2020.

It is estimated that from 50% to 70% of household waste could be recycled or composted, but for the UK as a whole, the practicable figure is likely to be much lower.

Once collected, recyclable waste usually needs some processing in a materials reclamation facility (MRF) to separate materials by type and to bulk them up before they are passed to the secondary materials industries.

Similarly, compostable wastes need to be processed in open windrows or in enclosed reactors or buildings. The final compost then needs to be blended with other materials to form growing media or soil conditioners.

Like all waste management plants, MRFs and compost production facilities can both have a detrimental impact on the local environment and on the health of employees. Consideration at the design stage, and careful operation and the use of pollution abatement methods can reduce the former. Operator health can be safeguarded by adopting designs and operational procedures that minimize human contact with the wastes.

Waste recycling and composting can help to conserve materials and energy and, as such, contribute to sustainable development. They also divert materials from landfill, thus reducing non-sustainable waste management. However, recycling and composting can only treat part of the waste stream so, at best, can only be regarded as a partial solution to the wastes problem.

12   WASTE REDUCTION AND REUSE

12.1   Introduction

We have already looked at some of the environmental problems associated with waste and at the specific problems related to waste processing and disposal. It may seem obvious to you, but the only reason that we have to solve these waste management problems is because the waste is generated in the first place. As we said back in Section 1.2 our nomadic ancestors produced virtually no waste and waste was not a problem to them. Whilst some people are tempted to advocate a return to this prehistoric golden waste-free age, most of us would not be happy to reject the last 5000 years of progress that humanity has achieved.

Having said that, waste reduction and the reuse of waste can help to minimize the quantities of waste that have to be treated.

Waste reduction means not generating wastes in the first place and is firmly at the top of the wastes hierarchy that I referred to in Section 2.2. In industry this may mean adjusting production processes to avoid unwanted by-products. Equally, it could mean altering manufacturing and assembly processes to reduce the amounts of 'off-cuts' produced or improving quality control to reduce rejection rates.

Reuse simply means using a product for its original purpose more times than was originally intended by the manufacturer. In this chapter we will look at examples of both techniques in the home and in industry and commerce.

12.2   Waste reduction and reuse in the home

So much of waste reduction and reuse in the home is common sense that you are almost certainly already doing this without thinking about it. When you go shopping and answer 'no' to the question 'would you like it in a bag?' you are taking part in waste reduction. Also, consider the humble jam jar:

- a cook will reuse it by filling it with home-made preserves or chutneys;

- a parent will reuse it by giving it to a child for use as a paintbrush holder;

- a DIY enthusiast will use it to store screws and nails.

SAQ 25

Write down ways in which you already practise waste reduction and reuse. Then write down some additional steps you could take to reduce or reuse wastes in the home.

However, it is important to recognize that there are limits to the amount of waste reduction that people will carry out in the home. For example, there is much debate over the relative environmental benefits of using disposable and reusable nappies. While the answer to the question 'which is better?' is far from clear, there is no doubt that a move from disposable to cloth nappies would reduce the amount of household waste produced. However, disposable nappies are very convenient and easy to use and, as such, many consumers will exercise their right to buy and use them. Similarly, we cannot expect consumers (including you and I) to give up their right to buy pre-washed and packaged salads and ready meals, Easter eggs and Christmas wrapping paper just to reduce waste and other forms of environmental pollution.

12.3 Commercial and industrial waste reduction and reuse

It has been estimated that for every person employed in the UK, £650 per year is spent on disposing of industrial and commercial waste (The Open University, 2000). There are many more beneficial ways in which this money could be spent (reducing prices, increasing profits, increasing wages, safeguarding jobs, etc.), so employers and employees both share the incentive to reduce waste at work. This economic drive helps to account for the relatively high recycling rates achieved by businesses (see Chapter 4), but there are even stronger reasons for reducing and reusing wastes.

SAQ 26

A commercial company buys 11 tonnes (or 4200 reams) of paper each year at a cost of £840 per tonne. Of this, 30% ends up in letters, reports, etc. that are delivered to customers or stored by the firm's staff. The rest is disposed of to a waste management company that charges £45 per tonne to collect and landfill the paper. Compare the costs of the following three scenarios:

(a) the current situation;

(b) the introduction of double-sided printing for company reports, resulting in paper savings of 10%;

(c) the introduction of double-sided printing resulting in paper savings of 10% and sending the scrap paper to a recycling company which pays £10 per tonne for this type of paper.

The relatively simple example in SAQ 26 shows that waste reduction/ reuse can achieve a 14% reduction in paper purchasing and disposal costs and, in this case, at virtually no cost to the firm concerned.

There are many 'waste reduction clubs' and 'green business clubs' across the country whose members can work together and exchange ideas and experiences to reduce waste or other environmental impacts (energy use, water consumption, etc.). Some of these clubs are related to particular river catchment areas, where consultants have been brought in to help identify areas where savings could be made. Some success stories are listed below:

■ a Lancashire wallpaper manufacturer saved £750 000 per year in raw material and waste disposal costs by improving process control and by recycling one of their intermediate products;

■ a Manchester brewery invested £800 in water meters; the resulting water monitoring led to reductions of £54 000 a year in water and effluent charges;

■ a caravan manufacturer worked with its material suppliers to reduce hardwood consumption by 40 tonnes per year, and recycle 100 tonnes of cardboard and 800 m^3 of polystyrene a year.

You will also be pleased to know that the Open University practises what we preach in this course and is active in waste reduction, for example:

- in 1998, 130 000 tonnes of paper was sent for recycling rather than to landfill;

- returnable packaging is used in Home Experiment Kits (another reason for taking care of your kit's packaging);

- waste cooking oil is recycled by a soap manufacturer;

- surplus office furniture is donated to a charity;

- green waste from the gardens and sports fields is composted.

Waste reduction and improvements in the use of other resources go hand-in-hand. For example, improvements in energy management systems at our Milton Keynes campus have reduced the use of heating oil by 40% and washroom water consumption has been reduced by 25% through replacing conventional taps with press-action taps.

Devising and implementing a waste reduction strategy will vary in complexity with the size of the business and the number of product and feedstock streams it deals with, but there are a number of key stages that are required in any scheme (see box).

WASTE REDUCTION STRATEGY DEVELOPMENT AND IMPLEMENTATION

1   Ensure real commitment and resources from top management.

2   Involve all employees in the process.

3   Identify the key waste streams and their current disposal routes.

4   Measure the weight of material in each waste stream.

5   Audit all disposal methods to ensure compliance with all current (and forthcoming) legislation.

6   Draw up a priority list for waste reduction.

7   Identify ways of reducing priority wastes (make use of: employee knowledge of the processes, the Environment Agency, published case studies, consultants).

8   Implement technically feasible and cost-effective solutions identified in Step 7.

9   Return to Step 3 and continue for as long as you wish to remain profitable.

12.3.1   Waste exchanges

Where there's muck there's brass.

Traditional Yorkshire saying

From this traditional Yorkshire saying we are reminded that wastes can have a value. *Waste exchanges* exploit this fact by turning one organization's waste into another organization's raw material.

In principle, waste exchanges are very simple. The exchange produces a list of organizations producing wastes with details of the quantities and specifications of the waste. This list is then circulated to potential users of the waste. If a provider and user can be matched up, the material is then transferred, saving the producer the cost of disposal and the user the cost of the raw material.

The 'waste' could be anything from chemicals to containers or computers to construction waste. The quantities can also range from a few kilograms on a one-off basis, to tonnage quantities at weekly intervals.

Some waste exchanges cover the entire country while others concentrate on a single county. A given exchange may focus on a particular type of material (construction and demolition waste, chemicals, etc.) or it may deal in different types of waste.

Some exchanges have a limited life. They may make all the logical matches between waste generators and users in the first few months of operation. At this point new arrangements tend to stop and the exchange is wound up. Other exchanges are more pro-active and develop new links by carrying out waste audits or acting as waste carriers.

Enter the term 'waste exchange' in an Internet search engine and find out how many UK-based exchanges are listed. Visit some of the sites to find out what types of materials are traded. Then look at the case studies below.

WASTE EXCHANGE CASE STUDY 1 – SOUTH WESSEX WASTE MINIMISATION GROUP

This venture is based in Blandford Forum and is aimed at helping firms in Dorset and Wiltshire. As well as running the waste exchange, the Group provides advice on waste minimization and acts as a source of information on improving a firm's environmental performance.

The exchange handles chemicals, plastics, paper and card, metals and wood. Recent waste transfers include:

- a metals company supplying another firm with plastic drums saving the supplier £250 per week in disposal charges;
- an aircraft services company giving fuelling hoses to a waste management company for use in a landfill gas collection scheme;
- a brewery supplying another firm with used bubblewrap.

WASTE EXCHANGE CASE STUDY 2 – WASTE EXCHANGE SERVICES

WES was founded in 1990 and specializes in chemical waste management, provides consultancy services to the chemicals industry and acts as a broker for the sale of surplus chemicals. The waste exchange includes several thousand materials on offer from aluminium oxide to waxed paper.

For further details visit the website at http://www.wasteexchange.com/

WASTE EXCHANGE CASE STUDY 3 – DETR MATERIALS EXCHANGE

This exchange deals in construction and demolition wastes. It also lists forthcoming demolition contracts and the materials likely to be produced. For example, on 9 May 2002 large quantities of soil were available in Leeds, a Northampton company was supplying gravel, and a Midlands company had several thousand metres of floorboards available.

For further details visit the website at http://cig.bre.co.uk/connet/mie/

12.4   Summary

Waste reduction avoids the problems of waste by not producing it in the first place. As householders, we can do much to reduce our waste production without too much effort. Industry and commerce can make great savings by implementing waste minimization strategies, often at little cost. Waste exchanges can assist by finding instances where one firm's waste can become another firm's raw material.

Waste reduction is inherently sustainable and can do much to reduce the need for waste management. However, a zero-waste economy remains a dream and the contribution of waste reduction should not be over-estimated.

13 MUNICIPAL WASTE MANAGEMENT COSTS

13.1 Conventional costing

Establishing the cost of managing a particular waste stream by any given method is fraught with problems. There is no standard method for calculating these costs, and businesses, local authorities and pressure groups all generate cost data to support their own particular views. For example:

■ costs can be commercially sensitive, so waste management companies are often unwilling to release detailed information;

■ the compilation and publication of local authority performance indicators by central government encourages local authorities to show their waste management costs in the most positive light;

■ it is not always clear whether particular figures include any element of profit and what the profit margin is;

■ published cost data are often based on theoretical exercises rather than on real-world experiences;

■ it is not always clear what assumptions are made about income from sales of reclaimed materials or energy;

■ some published costs do not include all the associated costs (for example, local authority figures do not always include all the relevant staff costs);

■ different organizations deal with the financing of capital equipment in different ways and this will influence the costs.

In short, you should treat all published waste management costs with a healthy degree of scepticism – even the costs I report below!

Waste management costs are usually broken down into collection costs and treatment costs. Collection costs cover the capital costs of the collection vehicles and bins, the operating cost of the vehicle and the wages (plus associated overheads such as national insurance, pensions, etc.) of the collection crews. Processing costs comprise the capital cost of the MRF, landfill, incinerator, etc., and the plant operating and staff costs.

The most up-to-date published figures were produced by the consultants Enviros Aspinwall for use in the Government's waste strategy (Defra, 2000). The figures are shown in Table 22. You will see that the collection costs are dependent on the type of area (rural, suburban or urban) and, in the case of recycling and composting, on the percentage of households participating in the scheme.

SAQ 27

Why are the compost collection costs so high and why do they have such a wide range of values?

SAQ 28

How might waste collection costs be reduced for recycling and composting schemes?

Table 22   Waste management costs

Option	Cost (£ per tonne)		
	Urban	Suburban	Rural
Collection			
Recycling (75% participation)	61	79	105
Recycling (55% participation)	66	84	111
Composting (75% participation)	87	119	178
Composting (55% participation)	97	131	198
Landfill	15	21	33
Incineration	15	21	33
Treatment and disposal costs			
Recycling	17–23	17–23	17–23
Composting	10	10	10
Landfill	25	25	15
Incineration	48	48	48
Total gross costs			
Recycling	78–84	96–102	122–8
Composting	97–107	129–41	188–208
Landfill	40	46	48
Incineration	63	69	81

It is important to note that the values shown in Table 22 are gross costs, which exclude the landfill tax costs and the income from materials and electricity sales. If we make the following assumptions about these values we can plot a range of net costs for each management option:

■ landfill tax rate of £15 per tonne (the figure for 2004);

■ recycled material income ranging from zero to £29 per tonne;

■ compost income ranging from zero to £10 per tonne of compost;

■ incineration power sales income from zero to £15 per tonne of waste burned;

■ landfill gas power sales income from zero to £1 per tonne of waste landfilled.

It may seem unduly pessimistic to assume that reclaimed power and materials have no value, but it is useful to consider this extreme position in determining the worst possible case. It can even be argued that the worst possible case is a negative income as, in recent years, recyclers have had to pay merchants to take reclaimed paper and plastics.

The effects of making the above adjustments are shown in Figure 29. From this we can see that, in the best possible case, composting proves to be the most costly option and there is little difference in the costs of the other schemes. However, under worst case conditions landfill costs are relatively unaffected, composting and recycling costs more than double and incineration costs almost double.

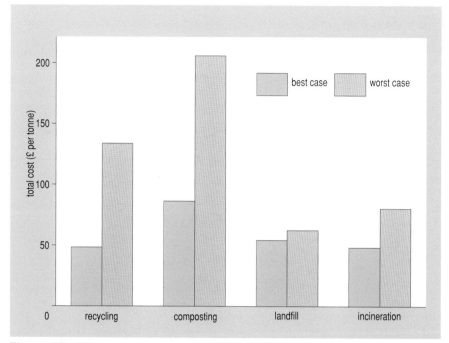

Figure 29 Waste management cost ranges

13.2   External costs

The costs discussed above are all 'internal' or 'private' costs. That is, they represent the amount of money that changes hands when particular goods or services are provided. This method of costing has been used since time immemorial and is used by all businesses and national economies, but it does have some important deficiencies. Internal costs make no attempt to allow for the depletion of finite resources or the environmental damage that might be caused when these resources are used. For example, the cost of a litre of petrol does not include a sum that is 'put away' against the day when there is no more petrol available. Equally, it does not include any specific amount to be spent on combating the effects of global warming.

The concept of 'external costs' is used to allow for these factors. For example, a 'carbon tax' could be levied on fuels according to their carbon content and the money collected used to improve coastal defences or to fund renewable energy developments.

SAQ 29

Make a list of the external costs that you might associate with municipal waste incineration. Don't forget that you may identify some environmental benefits from the process and you should include these. However, where there is a benefit, the external cost will be negative.

To some extent all waste management options yield environmental benefits in some areas, e.g. fossil fuel savings (from incineration and landfill gas) and resource conservation from recycling, composting and incineration. Equally, all options use finite resources in terms of fuel and materials. They also all lead to varying amounts of air, water and ground pollution.

External costing involves identifying the external costs and benefits and quantifying them by attaching a monetary value to each one.

Calculating external costs involves making assumptions about the 'values' of human life, health and resources and the cost of global warming and other types of pollution. It can also include assigning costs to the depletion of habitats and elimination of species of plants and animals that may or may not have any economic value to humankind. This is very subjective and a detailed discussion of the subject is beyond the scope of this course. Experts beginning from the same starting point often come up with completely different conclusions simply by making different assumptions about the cost of global warming, acidification, *eutrophication*, etc. However, we can say that:

■ recycling has a negative external cost (i.e. it is an environmental benefit);

■ landfill usually has a positive external cost (i.e. it is environmentally damaging); and

■ incineration external costs are negative or positive (depending on the conventional fuel saved by the incinerator, whether the energy recovered is in the form of heat and/or power and the location of the plant).

13.3   Summary

The cost of operating waste collection and management systems is often commercially sensitive information, so reliable values are not readily available. However, government figures suggest that waste collection costs range from £15 to £200 per tonne of material collected and processing/disposal costs from £10 to £50 per tonne. These costs also ignore reductions that could be made by integrating the collection of (say) recyclable material and residual waste in a single vehicle.

When landfill tax and any income from the sale of materials, composts and energy are taken into account the range of costs are:

Landfill	£50–£55 per tonne
Incineration	£45–£70 per tonne
Recycling	£50–£140 per tonne
Composting	£90–£210 per tonne

The concept of external cost is used to take account of non-renewable resource use or conservation, fossil fuel use or conservation and other forms of environmental pollution which conventional economics tend to ignore.

14 INTEGRATED SOLID WASTE MANAGEMENT

14.1 Principles

So far I have looked at the management of municipal and other wastes as a series of separate processes. I have done this deliberately so you can appreciate the technology involved in each process and, equally importantly, understand the limitations of each option. Just to remind you:

- Landfill is the cheapest method of disposing of MSW and can handle the whole waste stream, but it is the least sustainable method, has a high potential for causing environmental pollution and, apart from gas recovery, does not allow the reclamation of energy or materials. Furthermore, legislation is beginning to restrict the use of landfill for MSW.

- Incineration (or energy from waste) is an extremely well-developed technology, can treat virtually all the MSW stream, and recovers energy and metals and aggregate for recycling. It also results in at least a 70% reduction in the volume of residual waste sent to landfill. However, incineration can be unpopular with the public, obtaining planning authorization can be a problem and the process produces residues that can be difficult to deal with.

- Materials recycling and composting are popular with the public and can achieve high rates of materials reclamation. But only about 20–25% of MSW can be recycled and 15–20% composted. This is reliant on finding markets for the products and requires a high degree of commitment from householders. Recycling can also be an expensive option.

- Novel technologies such as anaerobic digestion and thermolysis have the potential for recovering energy and materials from waste and may have environmental advantages over current systems. These techniques are untested and may prove to be less attractive in practice. Also, given the lack of existing experience, a local authority or company that adopted one of these systems would have to accept the risk that the process may not perform to expectations.

From this summary we can see that there is no single solution to the problem of dealing with our wastes. Unfortunately, the debate over waste management has become very polarized. Proponents of recycling (often led by single-issue pressure groups) claim that unrealistic recycling rates can be achieved and that energy from waste will present an unacceptable risk to public health. On the other hand, some supporters of incineration understate the role that recycling can play.

When planning waste management systems, the question that we should be asking is not

> which one of these solutions should we adopt?

but

> how can we use these complementary technologies to solve our problem with the lowest impact on human health and the environment, and at the lowest cost?

In this chapter, we look at ways of answering this vital question.

14.2 Assessing the options

In the previous chapters we looked at the proportions of the waste stream that can be treated by a given method and the environmental impacts of each solution. What we need to do now is to consider and quantify all the environmental emissions that are generated or eliminated by each waste management option. Once we have done that, we can begin to look at ways of integrating the options to give the optimum solution – this process is called integrated solid waste management.

There is a danger that this exercise could turn into a version of 'the house that Jack built'...

> This is the carbon dioxide released in mining the coal that smelted the iron that produced the steel that went into the dustcart that delivered the waste to the MRF.

Fortunately there are tools that help us and one of the most widely used ones is the technique known as 'life cycle inventory assessment' (sometimes called *life cycle analysis* or LCA). The two leading waste-related LCA packages in the UK are the Environment Agency's WRATE (Waste and Resources Assessment Tool for the Environment) tool and the 'IWM 2' model developed by Procter and Gamble. Typical outputs from a waste LCA model are shown in Figure 30.

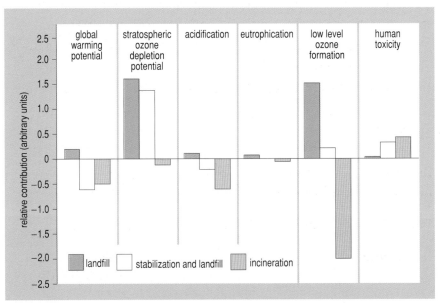

Figure 30 Waste LCA model outputs (source: Soyez *et al.*, 2001)

This example compares three options: direct landfill, stabilization (a crude composting process) followed by landfill, and incineration. Note that precursors of ozone, such as VOCs and NO$_x$ are emitted from landfills and landfill flares, and from engines at the landfill site.

While these outputs are helpful in assessing and selecting a waste management solution they do not provide the whole answer. For example, in Figure 30 we can see that incineration is the best option when considering ozone depletion in the stratosphere, acidification and ozone formation in the lower atmosphere, whilst stabilization gives the lowest contribution to global warming and landfill has the lowest human toxicity impact. In deciding which option to choose, we would need to look at local environmental and health priorities and, of course, consider the cost of each option.

The problem arises when we are seeking the 'best' solution without any constraints on a particular pollutant. To do this we need a technique that allows us to compare apples and pears – one which enables us to say that 'X kg of sulphur dioxide discharged to the air is equivalent to Y g of BOD discharged to a watercourse.' A detailed discussion of the techniques used is beyond the scope of this course, but you should note that methods are available and these often calculate the monetary value of the harm done to human health and to the environment by each discharge to provide a basis for comparison.

14.3   Integrating energy and materials recovery

One important question that must be addressed when considering integrated waste management is whether incineration and recycling can be combined to produce an integrated solution. Alternatively, does incineration prevent effective recycling and vice versa?

To answer this we need to consider the effect that a recycling scheme could have on the quantity of waste remaining and on its calorific value. In SAQ 30 you are asked to carry out the first stage of the calculation.

SAQ 30

Returning to the example in SAQ 6, calculate the proportion of material available for incineration for the following recycling scenarios:

(a) 40% of the paper/card, 25% of the dense plastic, 80% of the glass and 50% of the metals are recycled;

(b) 75% of the kitchen and garden waste is recycled by composting;

(c) recycling of both the 'dry' material from (a) and the 'wet' material from (b).

The next stage is to determine the calorific value of the remaining waste. Table 23 shows typical calorific values of the main components in UK MSW.

Table 23   Typical gross calorific values of MSW components

Component	Calorific value (MJ kg^{-1})
Paper and card	12.58
Plastic film	23.6
Dense plastics	26.7
Textiles	15.9
Miscellaneous combustible	11.6
Miscellaneous non-combustible	2.8
Kitchen and garden waste	5.5
Fines	4.8
Metals, glass, electrical/electronic equipment	0

SAQ 31

Use the information in Table 23 and your answers to SAQ 30 to calculate the calorific value of the waste available for incineration in the cases of the removal of:

(a) the construction and demolition waste, electrical/electronic equipment and potentially hazardous material;

(b) the fractions in (a) along with the recyclable material extracted in scenario (c) of SAQ 30.

SAQs 30 and 31 have identified two key points. Firstly, intensive recycling collections can potentially reduce the mass of material available for incineration and, secondly, such recycling schemes can increase the calorific value of the waste. These effects are not a problem if taken into account while designing incineration plant. Given the need for reductions in landfill under the landfill directive, many waste disposal authorities will have to increase recycling and composting and build incinerators. The different technologies are not competing, as you will see in the case study below.

Many parts of the country are now drawing up and implementing integrated waste management strategies. One of the most advanced schemes of its kind is Project Integra in Hampshire.

Project Integra is a major success story, and as the national waste strategies and landfill directive are implemented, schemes such as this one will become the norm rather than the exception. However, there was strong opposition to parts of the project, particularly the use of incineration. Both the Portsmouth and Southampton facilities required lengthy public enquiries during the planning process and the latter was also the subject of a Judicial Review in the High Court.

Log on to your local authority's website and see if you can find any references to the development of an integrated waste management strategy.

CASE STUDY – PROJECT INTEGRA

At the end of the 1980s, it became clear to the local authorities in Hampshire that they would soon be facing a waste disposal crisis. Landfill space was rapidly filling up, the incinerators built in the 1970s were not going to meet proposed European emission regulations and waste levels were continuing to increase.

In 1993, Hampshire County Council and the district councils undertook a county-wide public consultation process to find out the views of the residents of the county on how to deal with the waste problem. The consultation process resulted in the proposed integrated waste management strategy known as Project Integra.

Project Integra was adopted by the 11 district councils of Hampshire and the Portsmouth and Southampton unitary authorities. After a tendering process, the waste management company Hampshire Waste Services (a partnership between Hampshire County Council and Onyx Environmental Group) was awarded the contract to implement the project.

The overall aim of Project Integra is to provide an environmentally sound, cost-effective and reliable way of dealing with Hampshire's household waste. More specifically, the project has set itself the following targets:

- to stabilize household waste production at the 1995 levels;

- to achieve a recycling and composting rate of 40%;

- to reduce the amount of household waste disposed of to landfill to 25% of the total.

These aims are to be achieved by:

- expanding the provision of kerbside collection of materials for recycling;

- establishing a network of collection points for compostable waste at civic amenity sites;

- promoting waste minimization (including home composting) by means of publicity campaigns;

- building three MRFs, two centralized composting plants and three energy from waste incinerators.

The following progress has been made:

- over 90% of all households in the county are served by kerbside collection schemes;

- Two MRFs, three composting plants and three energy from waste incinerators have been built and are operating successfully.

In the year 2005/06, Project Integra achieved a household waste recycling rate of 32% and a recovery rate of 81%.

14.4   Summary

We have seen that no single waste management option can provide the ideal solution to the problem of wastes. The concept of integrated solid waste management involves using a combination of recycling, composting, incineration, landfill and novel techniques that provides the environmentally optimum solution at an affordable cost. Techniques such as life-cycle inventory assessment can help in determining what this optimum solution is.

Local authorities are beginning to develop and implement integrated solid waste management solutions. These tend to include measures to promote waste reduction, challenging but realistic targets for recycling and composting, incineration of the bulk of the remaining wastes that cannot be recycled, and landfill of the final residual wastes.

15   HAZARDOUS WASTE TREATMENT

We considered the subject of hazardous waste in Chapter 5 and in the following pages we will be considering how the waste management options that we looked at previously can be applied to hazardous wastes. We will also consider novel technologies that have been developed to deal with specific types of hazardous waste.

15.1   Landfill

The basic principles of landfill operations have been described in Chapter 8 in relation to municipal solid waste (MSW). However, the disposal of hazardous waste on land poses additional problems, depending on the materials deposited.

15.1.1   Regulation

Until recently, liquid and semi-liquid industrial wastes, including hazardous wastes, were often disposed of in co-disposal landfill sites. In these sites the waste was discharged in controlled quantities in trenches formed in previously deposited MSW. Because of its high absorptive capacity the MSW soaked up the liquid. The mixed wastes then behaved as a 'bioreactor' and the organic components of the industrial waste were broken down by micro-organisms in the same way as the components of MSW are degraded (see Section 8.1). In addition, the MSW absorbed and immobilized heavy metals and other potentially polluting species such as acids or alkalis in the industrial waste. Limited testing has suggested that the leachate from a co-disposal site is little different from that leaving a domestic waste site.

However, the landfill directive bans the landfilling of any liquid waste and also specifies that hazardous wastes may only be deposited at a site classified as a hazardous waste site. Therefore the practice of co-disposal has now ceased.

The directive also outlaws the following types of substance for use as landfill:

- explosive, corrosive, oxidizing, highly flammable or flammable substances (see Section 5.2);

- infectious hospital and veterinary wastes;

- tyres;

- certain types of chemical substances arising from research or teaching.

As demonstrated by the first item in this list it is clear that many hazardous wastes are not considered suitable landfill materials.

15.1.2   Site construction and operation

The landfill directive specifies several engineering measures that must be applied at hazardous waste landfills. These are listed in Table 24.

15.1.3   Other factors to be taken into account

The implementation of the landfill directive should eliminate many of the problems described below. However, it is important to consider these problems in relation to developing land or abstracting water from the neighbourhood of a site that was operational before the implementation of the landfill directive, when many of the controls would not have been in place.

Table 24 Hazardous waste landfill design requirements

Leachate sealing layer	Required
Drainage layer between the sealing layer and waste	Required
Artificial sealing layer at the surface	Recommended
Impermeable surface layer	Recommended
Drainage layer above the seal	Recommended
Final topsoil cover	Recommended

Air pollution

Many organic materials are malodorous and can cause a smell nuisance. Toxic substances produced by reactions can escape off-site, and dust containing heavy metals or asbestos presents a health risk if allowed to blow around. Measures should be implemented to prevent the creation of wind-borne fugitive emissions when landfilling powders or other light materials.

Water pollution

MSW sites, as we have seen, can give rise to water pollution, but some of this is treatable. Organic materials and some inorganic compounds such as ammonia can be dealt with by leachate treatment plants described in Chapter 8 and in Block 3. Materials leaking from older sites containing hazardous wastes may pose more serious threats to water supplies. There have been some instances of organic solvents contaminating aquifers in the UK and, on a much more widespread basis, in the USA. Cleaning up such contamination is difficult and expensive – and may not always be possible. A survey carried out in the 1980s by the UK Atomic Energy Authority of 100 landfill sites found that most sites (62%) took no measures to prevent groundwater ingress, and 54% performed no monitoring of groundwater (Croft and Campbell, 1990). More than 50% of sites had no boreholes to monitor within-waste leachate levels. Typically, there was less than one groundwater monitoring borehole per kilometre of site perimeter. Only 20% of sites had their groundwater monitored by the (then) water authority, compared with 47% of sites which had their surface waters monitored. Most sites had no means of intercepting or collecting leachate.

In roughly a third of sites surveyed by the UK Atomic Energy Authority there was no definitive information to quantify any problems due to leachate. Of those which performed some monitoring, more than half had experienced surface or groundwater contamination, and of these, only half had taken action to control the problem. Many approaches were tried by sites which had taken action, and all but one site managed to control leachate problems adequately. Proportionally, most reported problems occurred in dilute-and-disperse sites. Almost all groundwater contamination incidents were related to such sites, while containment sites had proportionally more surface contamination incidents.

Leachate attenuation

Modern landfill sites should be designed to control the rate of release of leachate into the environment, but leaks cannot always be ruled out. Also, as you saw above, older sites may not be equipped with liners or mechanisms to capture leachate.

However, even when leachate is discharged from a landfill site the following natural processes tend to reduce the impact of such a discharge.

■ Dilution – where high groundwater flow rates dilute the leachate so that the concentrations of harmful components are greatly reduced. This is effective in saturated rock formations, but not so in the unsaturated zone where the availability of additional water is limited. It must be remembered that the bioaccumulation of persistent pollutants may subsequently occur.

■ Adsorption – by which charged species, such as metal ions, are held onto the surfaces of soil and rock particles or even other components of the waste such as paper. The degree of adsorption will depend on the nature of the ion, the nature of the surface and the prevailing pH (a fall in pH can release previously adsorbed species).

■ Absorption – by which material is held within the body of another material, e.g. the pores of a rock or a mass of organic material such as paper.

■ Ion exchange – by which a toxic metal in solution is exchanged for a less toxic ion in a mineral structure. Clays can be particularly effective at trapping metals in this way and ion-exchange is the basis of a number of water purification and effluent treatment processes.

■ Filtration – where suspended material, including bacteria, are left behind as the leachate flows through a rock mass that has very fine pores.

■ Chemical reactions – such as neutralization, in which acidic materials react with alkaline rocks or soil. This may be followed by precipitation of dissolved metal ions as the pH rises.

■ Biodegradation – aerobic micro-organisms in the unsaturated zone may oxidize some organic species providing that the leachate is not toxic to them. This can reduce the amount of harmful material reaching an aquifer. The products of oxidation are mainly carbon dioxide and water with some nitrate if ammonia is oxidized (nitrified). Once the oxygen in the unsaturated zone is used up, anaerobic organisms take over and carbon compounds are metabolized to methane. Sulphur compounds appear as hydrogen sulphide and the result of both types of process is an increase in microbial biomass.

However, these natural mechanisms do not always provide an adequate safeguard. Some materials are not readily attenuated – chlorinated solvents, for instance, are non-polar (see Section 6.5 of Block 0: *Chemistry*) and are hence not readily adsorbed by clay minerals. They are also resistant to oxidation. Such compounds have caused severe aquifer pollution at a few sites in Britain leading to costly remediation works. Attenuation may be reversible in some instances if conditions change. There will also be a maximum amount of material that can be held by a given thickness of soil or rock. Once this attenuation capacity is exhausted, toxic materials may flow through relatively unimpeded and cause pollution. It will then become necessary to reduce the concentration of pollutants in the leachate.

SAQ 32

List the principal mechanisms responsible for attenuating the harmful components of leachate from a landfill site. Which are reversible and which are irreversible?

15.2   Incineration

In Chapter 9, we looked at the incineration of municipal wastes. This technique can also be used to treat flammable hazardous wastes although there are a number of important differences between the two types of system.

There are two merchant hazardous waste incinerators in England. These burn wastes produced by organizations that do not have their own in-house facilities. Materials treated this way include agro-chemical wastes, halogenated wastes, oils containing PCBs, solvents, laboratory chemicals and acid tars. Sometimes these materials are blended with non-flammable aqueous hazardous wastes by the incinerator operators to produce a mix that can be burned.

In addition there are 14 in-house hazardous waste incinerators in England and Wales that only burn wastes produced on their own sites. These burn a range of wastes including resin-containing liquids, spent catalysts, industrial gases, explosives, liquids containing volatile organic compounds, and contaminated soils and wastes from the pharmaceutical and petrochemical industries.

For organic wastes, incineration can represent a means of virtually total destruction. The molecules are completely oxidized to carbon dioxide, water and other (minor) components such as sulphur dioxide, nitrogen oxides or oxides of phosphorus, depending on the other elements present in the organic material. Properly controlled, a hazardous waste incinerator can operate at a destruction and removal efficiency (DRE) of over 99.9999% and very little air pollution need be created. The DRE is calculated by comparing the amount of a given compound in the effluent gases with the amount fed into the incinerator. It is usually done for difficult-to-burn materials such as polychlorinated biphenyls (PCBs). The assumption is made that, if PCB molecules are destroyed (broken down to simpler compounds) with a DRE of 99.9999%, other organic materials are broken down even more effectively.

The principal features of a modern hazardous waste incinerator are shown in Figure 31. Note that this system uses a wet scrubbing device and has a process for treating the scrubbing liquor.

Hazardous waste incinerators differ in design from MSW incinerators in several respects. They are normally designed to deal with pumpable wastes or those that can be emptied into the plant via drums. They do not, therefore, need agitators or rollers to stir the wastes to ensure thorough combustion. Turbulent mixing is usually ensured by controlling the flows of air, fuel and waste within the combustion chambers, although the *rotary kiln* also agitates the waste as it burns by virtue of its movement.

Air pollution control

The materials handled by a hazardous waste incinerator may contain a range of elements capable of causing air pollution – and land contamination when deposited. Heavy metals may be present and these

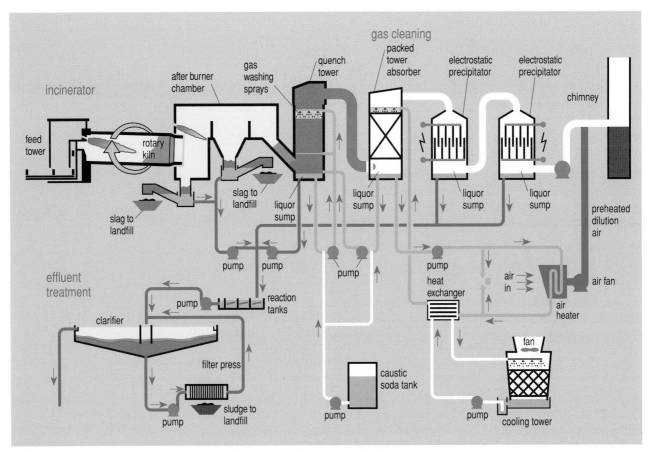

Figure 31   Hazardous waste incinerator

will either volatilize during combustion or be carried out of the combustion zone as particulate matter. Non-metals such as sulphur and phosphorus form acidic oxides, while the high temperatures in the plant will ensure that some nitrogen oxides are formed. Of particular concern are compounds of chlorine since incomplete combustion of chlorinated organic compounds can lead to the production of chlorinated dioxins and dibenzofurans, some of which are highly toxic. Fluorine-containing compounds may also be hazardous because their combustion products include toxic fluorides and these may also accelerate corrosion in the plant.

Air pollution control in incinerators is achieved in two stages: during combustion and afterwards. The philosophy of combustion control is based on the 'three Ts' – temperature, time and turbulence:

■ The temperature in the incinerator must be tightly controlled and high enough to ensure that the activation energy for the breakdown of the waste molecules is exceeded and that sufficient time at high temperature is provided for the breakdown reactions to be complete. If the plant is to handle PCBs, it must be not less than 1100 °C, and plants not handling chlorinated wastes must maintain a temperature of 850 °C to ensure good combustion and prevent odour problems.

■ The time factor depends on the wastes to be burned, but for wastes likely to generate dioxins a residence time of two seconds in the hottest part of the combustion zone is required. Bulky wastes, such as drums and transformers, can take several hours to burn out, although the residence time criterion refers to the afterburner section.

■ Turbulence in the combustion zone is required to ensure that there are no 'cold spots' within which combustion may be incomplete and to ensure that sufficient oxygen is available throughout. This is achieved by careful design of the combustion chamber and the use of air or fuel/air jets at appropriate points.

To the 'three Ts' must be added a fourth factor: oxygen. Sufficient oxygen must be present to ensure complete combustion and this is achieved by pumping in more air than is theoretically needed according to the chemical equations for the combustion reactions. The gases leaving the combustion chamber are monitored to ensure that there is residual oxygen; if levels fall below a pre-set limit, more air is added. Some plants add pure oxygen instead of air.

Modern incinerators incorporate sophisticated computerized monitoring equipment to ensure that the combustion conditions lie within the stated parameters.

After combustion of the hazardous wastes is complete it is important to cool the gases as quickly as possible to prevent the formation of dioxins from residual materials in the waste stream. As energy recovery is not usually practised in hazardous waste incineration, this is achieved in a quench tower which sprays water into the gases, bringing their temperature down to around 80 °C within a few seconds. The quenching washes out some particulate matter and absorbs some gases, but specialized equipment is required to complete this process. Sodium hydroxide solution is used in a scrubber to absorb acidic gases, such as sulphur dioxide and hydrogen chloride, and an *electrostatic precipitator* removes most of the particulate matter. The waste gases are, by now, cool and damp, so they are reheated by the addition of hot air and discharged through a tall stack (sometimes an activated carbon filter is used as well, prior to discharge).

The solid residue from the incinerator – ash or a glassy slag, depending on the operating temperature – is non-hazardous and is usually landfilled. The filter cake produced from the slurry generated in the scrubber and the dust from the electrostatic precipitator (if a dry model is used) are usually landfilled as hazardous waste in a suitably licensed site.

Some specialist industrial waste incinerators may be used for materials reclamation. Metal-containing items such as copper cables may be burned under controlled conditions to remove insulating materials and the metals reclaimed. Some hazardous waste incinerators may be used as a source of heat but this is not generally the case in the UK.

The biggest problem with incineration is the disposal of the gas cleaning residues, as stated in Section 9.6. In future these residues will not be accepted for landfill without extensive secondary processing.

SAQ 33

Draw a flow chart illustrating the operation of a rotary kiln incinerator, including pollution control procedures.

SAQ 34

What particular pollution control problems might arise during the incineration of chlorofluorocarbons (CFCs)?

SAQ 35

A hazardous waste incinerator burns a mixture of wastes including transformer oils containing, on average, 2% PCBs. If 25 kg of this oil are burned per hour and the plant operates on a 24-hour basis, calculate the daily emissions of PCBs if the destruction and removal efficiency of the plant for PCBs is 99.9999%.

SAQ 36

Suggest three reasons why using pure oxygen rather than air to support combustion in a hazardous waste incinerator may be advantageous.

15.3   Use as a fuel

Contaminated oils may be classed as hazardous wastes depending on the level and nature of the contamination, but these oils still have a high calorific value and are potentially usable as fuels. In some important aspects cement kilns function like hazardous waste incinerators. They operate at a very high temperature and degree of turbulence, i.e. they achieve a high DRE. Also, the nature of the cement means that the environment is highly alkaline so the neutralization of any acid gases formed is highly efficient. Finally, cement kilns are also fitted with highly efficient electrostatic precipitators or other particulate abatement equipment.

Specialist firms are now producing substitute fuels from oils classed as hazardous wastes. The oils are produced to tightly controlled specifications and supplied to cement and lime kiln operators to use as a substitute for conventional oils. Given the nature of the material it can only be used in kilns that have been authorized by the Environment Agency. By September 2000 nine kilns were authorized to use these fuels on a permanent basis or in trials.

15.4   New technologies

A wide range of new technologies for hazardous waste management have been developed. Many of the innovations originate in the USA, partly as a result of government-sponsored research programmes. Techniques include thermal, electrochemical, chemical and biological treatments and some have reached the commercially viable stage. Many are expensive and hence are likely to be reserved for wastes that are particularly harmful and difficult to deal with such as dioxins and PCBs. A few are briefly described so that you have a nodding acquaintance with possible future developments.

15.4.1   Thermal techniques

The plasma torch

Plasmas are gases whose electrons have been stripped away from their atomic nuclei. A plasma can be generated by creating a spark between two electrodes. This ionizes the surrounding gas. The plasma can be generated either at very low or very high temperatures according to the pressure of the gas. A high-pressure system is a plasma torch (Figure 32), which uses an electric arc to generate very high temperatures (5000 °C to 10 000 °C), through which a stream of nitrogen gas is passed to provide a reducing atmosphere. Pumpable wastes are introduced into the gas stream and the constituent molecules are broken down into atoms and ions. When cooled, these recombine to form simple molecules or, in the case of some ions, lose charge to revert to atoms. The result is mainly carbon, carbon monoxide, hydrogen and, if chlorinated wastes are present, hydrogen chloride. Sodium hydroxide solution is used to scrub the gases, thereby removing hydrogen chloride, and the hydrogen and carbon monoxide can be used as a fuel. The system is portable: it fits into two articulated lorry trailers. It has not been used in the UK, although trials in the USA have proved successful. The destruction efficiency is quoted as greater than 99.99999% – better than many conventional hazardous waste incinerators. The plasma arc principle has also been extended to other systems, which are said to be capable of handling solid and semi-solid wastes such as sewage sludge, tyres and, in one instance, electrical capacitors containing PCBs.

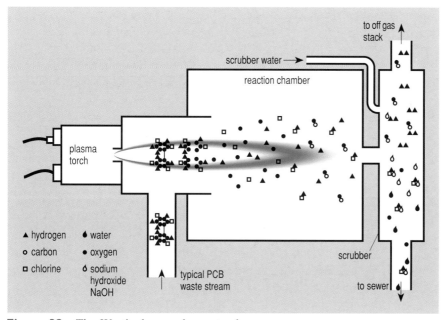

Figure 32   The Westinghouse plasma torch

Infra-red heating

Another mobile technology for treating hazardous wastes is based on infra-red radiation. Waste is carried by conveyor into a primary heating chamber, where radiant heaters powered by electricity, dry and break down the wastes. The gases produced pass into a second chamber where a gas flame and more radiant heaters complete the destruction of the wastes. Air is pumped into the primary chamber to ensure that a sufficient excess of oxygen is present and the speed of the conveyor is controlled to adjust the residence time. A temperature of 1300 °C is possible, although the unit normally operates at around 900 °C. The exhaust gases must be scrubbed before discharge to the air, resulting in the residue disposal problems described in Section 15.2.

Pyrolysis

Some wastes are suitable for *pyrolysis* – heating in the absence of air – and this can be achieved in an infra-red unit or in a device known as an advanced electric reactor. In both cases air is excluded. The lack of oxygen means that the simple breakdown products of the process are in a chemically reduced form (e.g. hydrogen and hydrocarbons), which can be drawn off and can be burned as fuel(s). Dioxins have been destroyed successfully in a demonstration-scale electric reactor and research is continuing. Refer to the Set Book for further information.

Supercritical water oxidation

At high temperatures and pressures water becomes a good solvent of oxygen and many organic compounds which are not usually water soluble. This is known as a supercritical state and is exploited in organic waste treatment. A mixture of wastes, oxygen and aqueous alkali is heated to 450 °C at about 250 atmospheres pressure, and the high concentrations of dissolved oxygen rapidly oxidize hydrocarbons and other organic materials. Chlorine, phosphorus and sulphur are oxidized to weak acids; these are neutralized by the alkali and there are no significant emissions to the atmosphere. High destruction efficiencies have been reported from pilot-scale plants and the process is said to be suitable for organochlorine wastes. A lower temperature version of this process, where the water does not become supercritical, is 'wet air oxidation'. Temperatures and pressures are lower (although still much higher than normal) and the process is not as quick or efficient for some more-intractable wastes.

Other thermal processes

Other techniques involving the thermal breakdown of organic wastes include:

■ catalytic incineration systems, which can operate at lower temperatures than conventional incinerators;

■ the use of microwaves to generate plasmas;

■ solar reflectors, which focus the Sun's rays into a confined space, producing a very high temperature.

It must be remembered that inorganic wastes, whose hazard derives from the presence of toxic elements such as heavy metals and fluorine, cannot be destroyed by thermal means because the elements are not destructible. Thermal techniques can be used to immobilize some inorganic wastes. For instance, asbestos and heavy metals may be incorporated in a glassy solid produced in a modified glass furnace. However, burning a mixed waste containing both metals and organic matter only solves part of the problem. Indeed, it may create others because the metals are concentrated and volatilize on heating.

15.4.2   Chemical techniques

A range of chemical techniques can be used to destroy organic hazardous wastes. These fall into two main groups: dechlorination and complete oxidation.

Dechlorination

The noxious properties of many organic wastes derive from the presence of chlorine compounds. Once chlorine is removed, the residues are much easier to handle and may even be usable as fuel. The removal of chlorine from molecules can be achieved in a number of ways. Alkali metals such as sodium, calcium or potassium can be used to treat PCBs; the result being the ionic chloride of the metal and a combustible hydrocarbon. These metals can be dangerous to handle so they may first be reacted with an alcohol to produce compounds called alcoholates, which react more controllably with the chlorinated waste.

High-temperature steam and hydrogen are used to dechlorinate PCBs in transformer oils in the French Neostar process, which produces recoverable hydrocarbons and hydrochloric acid as a result. Hot alkali under pressure has been used for removing chlorine from PCBs in Japan. Hydrogen, in the presence of an appropriate catalyst, has also been used for dechlorinating PCBs and another process uses methane to achieve the same end. Transformer oils containing PCBs have also been treated using potassium hydroxide and solvents called polyethylene glycols.

As stated in Section 9.6 the disposal of residues containing chlorides will be a major problem in the future. Although chlorides are not hazardous, they are highly soluble and highly mobile. Therefore, they are only weakly attenuated by the processes described in Section 15.1.3. Dilution is basically the only way of dealing with the chloride-containing wastes.

Oxidation

Chemical reagents such as hydrogen peroxide, bleach (sodium hypochlorite) and even exotic reagents such as ruthenium tetroxide have been investigated as potential oxidants for waste treatment. One of the most successful examples is the 'Winwox' process developed by the UK Atomic Energy Authority for the processing of radioactive wastes at Winfrith, Dorset.

The Winwox process was designed to remove the organic components of intermediate level radioactive waste liquids and sludges. If these organic materials are not removed the decomposition processes can lead to the undesirable mobilization of radioactivity. Hydrogen peroxide is reacted with the liquid or sludge, preheated to 80 °C, in a batch process which does not need further heating since it is exothermic. A catalyst may be added, although metals present in the waste often serve this purpose. Oxygen, carbon dioxide, water and a little carbon monoxide are the by-products of the reaction, with chlorine and sulphur ending up as chlorides and sulphates in solution. The process is not confined to the treatment of radioactive wastes; a wide range of organic materials from other industries can be treated, although oils and plastics are, currently, difficult to handle. Cyanides may also be treated in this way.

15.4.3 Electrochemical incineration

Another process developed by the nuclear power industry is electrochemical incineration (Figure 33). Destruction of the waste is achieved by reacting it with silver (II) ions formed in an electrochemical cell. The electrolyte is dilute nitric acid containing a small quantity of dissolved silver which is normally present as silver (I) ions. As current flows, silver (I) is converted into silver (II) at the anode and this, together with the nitric acid, rapidly oxidizes organic materials dissolved or immersed in the liquid reducing the silver back to the silver (I) form and the nitric acid to nitrous acid. Further current flow regenerates the silver (II) ions and the nitrous acid is withdrawn and reoxidized from time to time. AEA Technology plc has developed the SILVER II™ commercial-scale process to treat a range of organic wastes including chemical weapons such as nerve gases and explosives. The US army is using SILVER II plants in trials to destroy weapons under the Chemical Weapons Convention.

15.4.4 Biological treatment

Theoretically, almost any carbon compound could be considered as a potential source of food for micro-organisms such as bacteria. In some instances, the toxicity of a waste may prevent bacteria from metabolizing it and, in other instances, the chemical structures in the waste may be so different from naturally occurring compounds that there are no ready-made enzyme systems present in living organisms capable of breaking them down. Nevertheless the biological treatment of some hazardous wastes, albeit dilute ones, is a reality and much research is under way in this area,

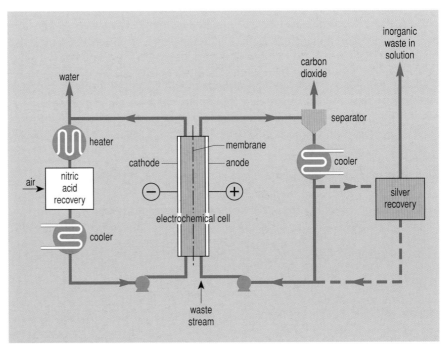

Figure 33   Electrochemical incineration

particularly in the context of cleaning up contaminated land (discussed further in Chapter 17).

The *activated sludge* process, as used in sewage treatment (discussed in detail in Block 3), can handle some hazardous wastes provided that the concentration of toxic material is not too high. This is an oxidation process and converts organic compounds to (mainly) carbon dioxide and water. Heavy metals tend to accumulate in the sludge leaving a cleaner liquid effluent, although this may aggravate the problem of sludge disposal. Anaerobic processes have also been used for some wastes with methane occurring as a potentially useful by-product.

Organochlorine compounds are difficult to handle biologically (they are rare in nature so organisms that can break them down have not evolved widely), but a range of organisms has been identified for treating these compounds. For example, the white rot fungus *Phanerochaete chrysosporium* can break down a variety of organochlorine compounds including PCBs, and cocktails of bacteria have been developed to digest PCBs and the herbicide trichlorophenoxyacetic acid (2,4,5-T). Further research may lead to the production of 'designer organisms' tailor-made to destroy particular wastes. Caution must be exercised in releasing genetically engineered micro-organisms into the environment, however, as there may be unforeseen risks.

SAQ 37

What are the main differences between the operation of a plasma torch waste-destruction unit and a high-temperature incinerator?

SAQ 38

List the techniques available, or under development, for the destruction of PCBs. State which are likely to be suitable for contaminated soils and which should be capable of handling liquid wastes, e.g. transformer oils.

SAQ 39

The following materials may appear as components of wastes. Which of them are likely to be amenable to biological treatment?

(a) acetic acid

(b) tetraethyl lead

(c) DDT

(d) phenol

(e) CFCs.

15.5   Summary

Hazardous wastes are usually disposed of by landfill, treated to reduce their hazardous nature, recycled or incinerated. Hazardous waste management facilities use the same principles as those that handle other wastes, but environmental pollution prevention and control provision is much more stringent.

16   RADIOACTIVE WASTE

16.1   Radioactive waste in the environment

According to A. J. Gonzalez, Radiation and Waste Safety divisional director of the International Atomic Energy Authority (IAEA):

> Like telling fingerprints the wastes we leave behind characterize our human civilization. They show the ways in which we live and how we care for the world around us.
>
> (IAEA, 2000)

What do you first think of when you hear the words 'radioactive waste'? Is it:

- the waste produced from the day-to-day operation of nuclear power stations?

- the waste produced after accidents at nuclear power stations such as the 1979 accident at *Three Mile Island* in the USA or the 1986 accident at *Chernobyl* in the former USSR?

- the waste produced from radioactive sources used in medicine?

- the waste present in the air we breathe, the food we drink or the food we eat produced through natural processes?

Or is it:

- the 'waste' from cosmic rays entering the Earth's atmosphere from outer space?

Each of these sources of radioactive waste can result in radioactivity and in exposure of the population, and can thus affect the health of humans and ecosystems.

With increasing concern about climate change and suggestions of a return to nuclear power it is vital to have a good understanding of nuclear processes and the hazards associated with handling and managing radioactive waste. In the following sections you will be exploring the nuclear processes that produce radioactivity, the process of radioactive decay and the implications for human health.

16.2   Nuclear processes

In this chapter I will look at three fundamental nuclear processes: nuclear fusion, nuclear decay and nuclear fission. These processes account for both the beneficial and harmful properties of nuclear materials and the particular problems that arise when dealing with nuclear wastes.

STUDY NOTE

If you are unfamiliar with the terms isotope, proton, neutron and nucleus it is worth reviewing Section 1.1 of Block 0: *Chemistry* before moving on.

16.2.1   Fusion processes

Let's start with radiation. Which types of radiation are you familiar with? You may have thought of visible light, X-rays or microwaves, each one having a characteristic wavelength (Figure 34).

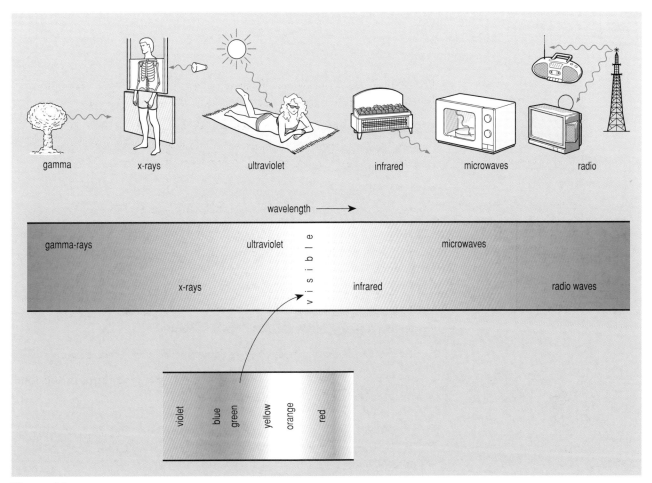

Figure 34

Solar radiation from the Sun provides the main source of energy for the Earth even though the Sun is 93 million miles (150 million kilometres) away. The process that releases thermal energy in the core of the Sun is called nuclear fusion.

Through this process light atomic nuclei *fuse* to form heavier ones. For example, in the nuclear fusion reaction given below, two isotopes of hydrogen combine to form helium, with the release of a neutron and a large amount of energy.

$$^2_1H + ^3_1H \longrightarrow ^4_2He + ^1_0n$$

^2_1H is the *isotope* of hydrogen, deuterium; and ^3_1H is the isotope tritium.

SAQ 40

What are the differences between deuterium ^2_1H and the more familiar form of hydrogen ^1_1H?

The difference between chemical reactions and nuclear fusion reactions (like the one described above) is that in nuclear fusion, a new element is produced (in this case, helium). There is also an overall difference in mass between the total rest mass of the two hydrogen nuclei and the total rest mass of the helium nucleus and the neutron produced. This change of mass is vital because it is related to energy. Einstein's theory of relativity, formulated in 1905, showed that 'an amount of energy (of any type) has

We use the term 'rest mass' because the mass of an object in motion increases, as described by Einstein's theory of relativity, but any further details are beyond the scope of this course.

an equivalent mass' and predicted that the mass m that is equivalent to energy E is given by

$$m = E/c^2$$

In its more familiar form, this is Einstein's equation $E = mc^2$

where

c is the speed of light, approximately 3×10^8 m s^{-1}

E is the energy in J (joules)

m is the mass in kg

The energy from nuclear reactions is normally given in electronvolts per reacting nucleus (eV) where 1 eV $= 1.602 \times 10^{-19}$ J.

In the reaction above, when a helium nucleus and a neutron are formed in the Sun's central core, mass is lost and therefore approximately 3.3 MeV $(3.3 \times 10^6$ eV) of energy is released. This can be compared with the 4 eV or 6.4×10^{-19} J per molecule of carbon dioxide released in the combustion of carbon.

Two nuclear 'power stations' are shown in Figure 35.

SAQ 41

Consider the two nuclear power stations shown in Figure 35. The Sun has a power output of 4×10^{26} W and Sizewell B has a power output of 1.2×10^9 W. How many nuclear power stations like Sizewell would be needed to match the Sun's output?

But if fusion produces so much energy, why don't we use fusion reactions as a source of energy? Well, a start has been made – a number of research projects are being undertaken across the world to produce controlled fusion reactions with the eventual aim of providing a source of energy. For example, the amount of energy that could be produced from deuterium (found in seawater) is massive, but there are immense technical problems to be overcome and it will be several decades (if ever) before we see this source of energy realized.

The fact is that it is not that easy to make two nuclei fuse. The reacting nuclei are both positively charged, so there is a large electrostatic repulsion between them as they come together. Only when they are squeezed very close to one another do they feel the strong nuclear force that can overcome the electrostatic repulsion and cause them to fuse. To bring two nuclei close enough for fusion to occur, a great amount of energy is required. One way this repulsive force is overcome in the core of the Sun is that there is a sufficiently high temperature and pressure, and thereby the necessary kinetic energy. As a result of these fusion reactions the Sun is estimated to contain about 70% hydrogen (by mass) and 28% helium. Some of this helium has been present since the formation of the Sun, with the remainder formed by the fusion processes.

It is generally understood that the fusion processes taking place within stars led to the formation of all the elements heavier than helium but lighter than iron. Heavier elements such as uranium 238 and uranium 235 are thought to have originated during the supernovae explosions that terminate the life of very large stars leading to the formation of new planets and stars. This implies that everything that is not H or He was once inside a star – this includes all the elements that you and I are made of.

(a)

(b)

Figure 35 (a) The Sun; (b) Sizewell B nuclear power station, Suffolk, England

16.2.2 Radioactive decay

The isotopes of all the naturally occurring elements were produced through the fusion processes. But are they all equally stable? Well, the answer is no, they're not.

Only certain combinations of protons and neutrons can exist as a nucleus. Figure 36 plots the number of neutrons ($A–Z$) versus the number of protons (Z) in the nuclei of stable isotopes, where A represents the atomic mass of the element. The slope of this graph is the ratio of neutrons to protons. The straight line shows the positions that isotopes with equal numbers of protons and neutrons would occupy.

Compare the ratios of neutrons to protons in $^{23}_{11}\text{Na}$ and $^{208}_{82}\text{Pb}$. There are 12 neutrons (i.e. 23–11) in the sodium 23 isotope, so the ratio of neutrons to

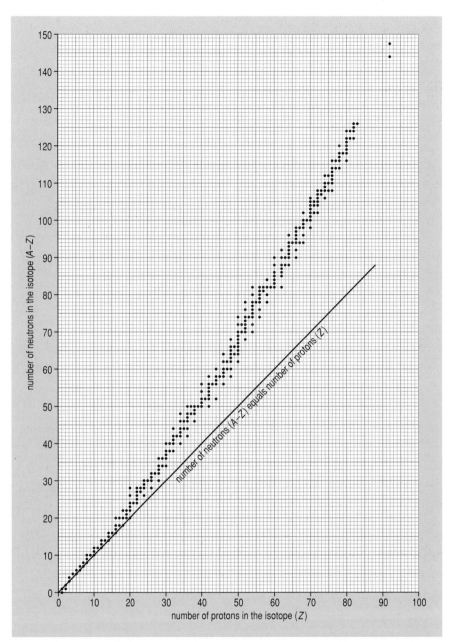

Figure 36   The variations in the number of protons and neutrons in the nuclei of stable isotopes. The straight line shows the positions that the isotopes with equal numbers of protons and neutrons would occupy. (source: The Open University, 1997, Figure 2.3, p.15)

protons is 12/11, that is 1.09. Whereas there are 126 neutrons (i.e. 208–82) in the lead 208 isotope, so the ratio in this case is 126/82, that is 1.54.

Stable isotopes occur in the narrow band shown in Figure 36. At the lower end, the numbers of protons and neutrons are the same. This tendency changes as the number of protons increases. The unstable nuclei that occur outside this band either have too many neutrons (the ratio of neutrons to protons is too large) or too many protons (the ratio of neutrons to protons is too small). $^{208}_{82}$Pb falls outside this band and is therefore likely to be unstable.

SAQ 42

Which of the following isotopes are likely to be unstable?

$^{14}_{6}$C, $^{14}_{7}$N, $^{22}_{10}$Ne, $^{22}_{11}$Na, $^{184}_{82}$Pb, $^{180}_{80}$Hg

---

If nuclei are unstable (i.e. they have too many protons or too many neutrons) they undergo the process of radioactive decay which changes their composition into a more stable form.

The way they decay depends on whether the nucleus has too many neutrons or too many protons for stability and these processes are discussed in the following paragraphs.

Beta-decay

Let us consider the first of these options where there are too many neutrons.

In this case, a neutron (n) can break down or decay to form a proton (p^+), an electron (e^-) and neutrino (v) as shown below

$$n \longrightarrow p^+ + e^- + v$$

A neutrino has no charge and very little mass so it can normally be neglected.

The decaying neutron is part of the nucleus and the proton produced stays in the nucleus, whereas the electron is ejected from the nucleus with considerable kinetic energy. The ejected electron is called a beta-particle (or β-particle), the nucleus decaying in this way is called a β-emitter, and the process is called β-decay.

So what happens to the atomic number of the nucleus as the result of this β-decay?

As we have seen from SAQ 42, $^{14}_{6}C$ is unstable and, because it has too many neutrons, it undergoes β-decay. The nucleus of carbon 14 has six protons, that is $Z = 6$, and it has eight neutrons ($A–Z$). When one of these neutrons decays into a proton and the electron is emitted the new nucleus will have seven neutrons and seven protons. The element with atomic number 7 (that is, with seven protons) is nitrogen; the new isotope will therefore be $^{14}_{7}N$ as shown below

$$^{14}_{6}C \longrightarrow {}^{14}_{7}N + e^- + v$$

Beta-decay therefore produces new isotopes and radiation from negatively charged β-particles. This negative charge of a particle is important. It means that when a β-particle passes through matter there will be an electrical force between the particle and the electrons and atoms of the surrounding matter. If the charges are the same, the force is one of repulsion; if they are different the force will be attraction. The force can be enough to eject one or more electrons from an atom's orbit and the atom will be left with a net positive charge (Figure 37). The atom is said

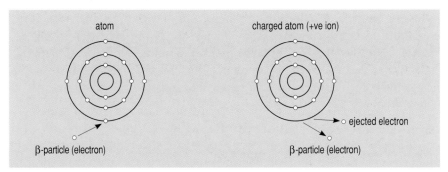

Figure 37 Example of ionization of an atom

to have been 'ionized', the process is called ionization and the radiation, such as β-radiation, that can cause damage in this way is one example of ionizing radiation.

This ejection of one or more electrons from the atom's orbit (ionization by radiation) differs from the 'ion formation' that you met in Block 0: *Chemistry*. When radiation donates energy to atoms or molecules, electrons other than those on the outermost orbit can be released, which makes the atoms very unstable. Such unstable atoms are called radicals and are chemically very reactive. Some radicals are so reactive that they exist only for a very short amount of time, in some cases microseconds.

In biological systems, β-rays lose energy as they pass through cells and interact with molecules. As the β-ray passes through a cell, it releases its energy along its path (called a track) by interacting with the electrons of nearby molecules. The released energy is absorbed by atoms near the track, and causes either excitation (a shift in the orbit of an electron to a higher energy level) or ionization (release of an electron from the atom), which can result in the creation of highly reactive radicals.

The β-emitters released during the nuclear accident at Three Mile Island in 1979 were the noble gases krypton 88 and xenon 133. Krypton 85 is continuously emitted from nuclear reprocessing plants such as the Thermal Oxide Reprocessing Plant (THORP) at Sellafield in the UK, and is a strong β-emitter.

The health implications of β-radiation and other forms of ionizing radiation will be discussed further in Section 16.3.

Gamma-decay

Gamma emission is usually a settling-down process by which a nucleus loses surplus energy, often following an α- or β-emission or fission. It does not change the numbers of protons or neutrons, so the two nuclei before and after γ-emission differ only in their energy.

But that's not quite the end of the story. In certain cases a proton breaks down to form a neutron, and a positively charged electron e^+ (a positron) is emitted according to the equation shown below

$$p^+ \longrightarrow n + e^+$$

The neutron will stay in the nucleus but the positron is emitted from it, often with considerable amounts of kinetic energy.

In positron emission a new element is formed with an atomic number that is one less than that of the decaying element, as shown by the decay of $^{22}_{11}Na$

$$^{22}_{11}Na \longrightarrow ^{22}_{10}Ne + e^+$$

Positron emission is used in diagnostic medicine in so-called positron emission tomography (PET). In this technique, a positron generated during the decay process described above encounters an electron. This encounter produces energy in the form of gamma rays (γ-rays) which, on detection, are used to produce an image. Gamma-rays are a high-energy form of radiation with no mass and no charge. Positron emission is quite unusual. In nearly all nuclear reactions, gamma rays are emitted as a form of energy with no mass and no charge, so no changes other than those shown by the beta decay are seen.

Alpha-decay

If a nucleus is unstable and has a high mass number and a high atomic number, it is possible for two neutrons and two protons to be emitted together so that the resulting nucleus has two fewer protons and two fewer neutrons. This means that the atomic number is reduced by two and the atomic mass is reduced by four. This combination of two protons and two neutrons is called an alpha particle (α-particle); the nucleus is called an α-emitter and the process is called α-decay.

Lead 184 undergoes α-decay to form the mercury (Hg) isotope and an α-particle $_2^4$He (i.e. a helium nucleus) as shown below

$$^{184}_{82}\text{Pb} \longrightarrow \ ^{180}_{80}\text{Hg} + \ ^4_2\text{He}$$

X-rays

There is one other common form of radiation – the X-ray. Unlike the other forms we have discussed, X-rays do not originate from naturally occurring unstable nuclei but are produced in X-ray machines. An X-ray machine contains a source of electrons. The electrons are emitted when the machine is turned on – they strike the tungsten collecting terminal in a vacuum tube and X-rays are released (Figure 38).

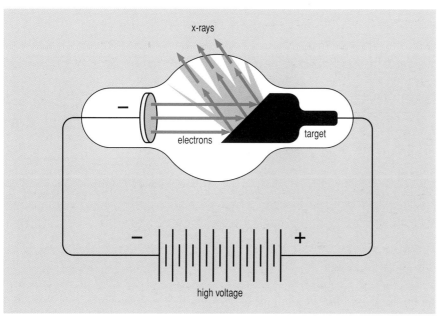

Figure 38 Anatomy of an X-ray machine (source: Chiras, 1998, p.264)

SAQ 43

A small sample of radioactive material that emits α-, β- and γ-radiation is placed between two parallel plates separated by an air gap. One plate is given a positive charge, the other a negative charge. (Remember that like charges repel each other and unlike charges attract.)

(a) Explain how the α-, β- and γ-radiation will move between these plates.

(b) If the arrangement were left to stand for a long time, explain why you would expect the plates to be no longer charged.

16.2.3 Modelling radioactive decay

As a result of α- and β-decay the atomic mass and activity of any radioactive material will be reduced. You can see this clearly in the neutron–proton diagram for the decay of $^{238}_{92}$U followed by the decay of the product $^{234}_{90}$Th to $^{234}_{91}$Pa, as shown in Figure 39.

This reduction can also be shown in terms of activity as in Figure 40, for example, where the activity decays exponentially with time.

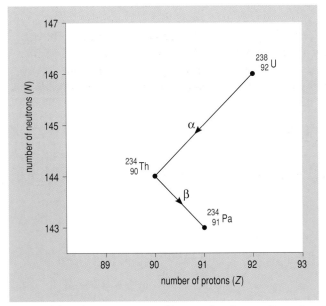

Figure 39 Neutron–proton diagram for decay of uranium 238

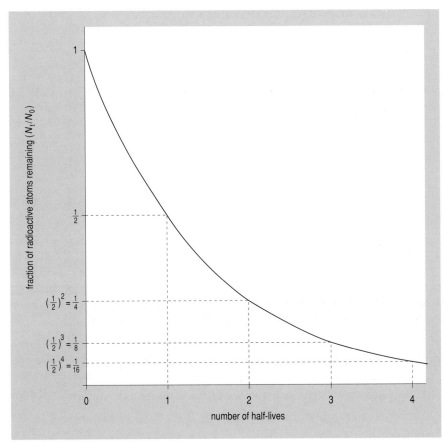

Figure 40 Radioactive decay

Mathematically this can be written as

$$N = N_0 \times e^{-\lambda t} \tag{1}$$

where

> N is the number of nuclei which have not decayed after a time t
>
> N_0 is the number of nuclei present initially (i.e. at $t = 0$)
>
> λ (lambda) is the radioactive decay constant.

An important property of exponential decay is that, irrespective of the number of unstable nuclei of a particular radioactive material present initially, the time taken for this number to halve will always be the same. The time for half the nuclei in a sample to decay – called the *half life*, $t_{1/2}$ – is a convenient and widely used measure of the rate of decay of radioactive isotopes

$$\text{So when } t = t_{\frac{1}{2}}, N = \frac{N_0}{2}$$

If we then use that case in Equation 1 we would get

$$\frac{N_0}{2} = N_0 e^{\left(-\lambda t_{\frac{1}{2}}\right)}$$

Dividing by N_0

$$\frac{1}{2} = e^{\left(-\lambda t_{\frac{1}{2}}\right)}$$

Taking logs (to the base e)

$$\ln\left(\frac{1}{2}\right) = -\lambda t_{\frac{1}{2}}$$

Using the log rules (from Block 0: *Mathematics and statistics*)

$$-\ln 2 = -\lambda t_{\frac{1}{2}}$$

so

$$\ln 2 = \lambda t_{\frac{1}{2}}$$

and

$$\lambda = \frac{\ln 2}{t_{\frac{1}{2}}}$$

If you are unsure about exponentials and this kind of manipulation take another look at Sections 3.3 and 3.4 in Block 0: *Mathematics and statistics*.

If this equation is then substituted into Equation 1, the decay equation becomes

$$N = N_0 e^{-\left(\frac{\ln 2}{t_{\frac{1}{2}}}\right)t} \tag{2}$$

To illustrate the application of Equation 2, suppose that a radioactive material of half life 0.5 hours has 100 nuclei initially. How many will it have after one hour?

From the given data

$$N_0 = 100$$

$$t_{\frac{1}{2}} = 0.5 \text{ hour}$$

$$t = 1 \text{ hour}$$

So, using Equation 2

$$N = 100 \times e^{-\left(\frac{\ln 2}{0.5}\right) \times 1}$$

$$= 100 \times e^{-1.386}$$

$$= 25$$

This numerically simple answer clearly illustrates the concept of half life; in the first half hour, the number of nuclei will halve from 100 to 50. Then in the second half hour, this 50 units will again halve to 25 units as calculated above.

SAQ 44

The uranium isotope $^{233}_{92}U$ decays in three separate reactions to the actinium isotope $^{225}_{89}Ac$. The reactions, in turn, emit an α-particle, a second α-particle, and a β-particle with the intermediate products being isotopes of thorium (Th) and radium (Ra).

(a) Write down the decay reactions for each of the three decays.

(b) Draw a neutron–proton diagram showing the overall decay mechanisms.

SAQ 45

The isotope of gold $^{198}_{79}Au$ decays by emission of a β-particle and a γ-ray with a half life of 2.7 days. The product is a stable isotope of mercury (Hg).

(a) Write down an equation for the decay reaction.

(b) Calculate the number of particles emitted per second by a source, initially of intensity 10^6 units, after it has been allowed to stand for seven days.

Hint: The intensity of a source is directly related to the number N of unstable nuclei so can be substituted in Equation 2.

16.3   Nuclear fission

In addition to the three decay processes outlined above, very high mass nuclei (such as uranium) can decay by spontaneous fission or by neutron-induced fission (when the nucleus collides with a neutron). These processes cause the original heavy nucleus to split into two smaller nuclei with the emission of one or more neutrons. Fissile isotopes such as uranium 235 and plutonium 239 undergo fission with neutrons of any energy and thus provide the raw materials for nuclear fission reactors and also for nuclear fission weapons. A large amount of energy (about 200 MeV) is released in each fission reaction as well as two or three neutrons, which make it possible for further fission reactions or a chain reaction to occur and thus obtain a further release of energy.

Nuclear weapons based on fission release very large amounts of energy in a few microseconds. For example, the bomb dropped on Hiroshima in 1945 contained about 64 kg of uranium and released the same amount of energy as 15 000 tonnes of TNT.

The same fission process is also the basis of nuclear power, where a self-sustaining chain reaction can be established in which the fission rate is constant. Fission reactions are held in check by a coolant, such as water, where water absorbs some of the neutrons, thus reducing the rate of fission. Control rods, e.g. slender rods of neutron-absorbing materials such as boron, lie between the fuel rods to control the overall speed of the reaction. The entire assemblage of fuel and control rods and coolant are housed in a thick reactor vessel surrounded by a shield and then contained within a reactor containment building as shown in Figure 41.

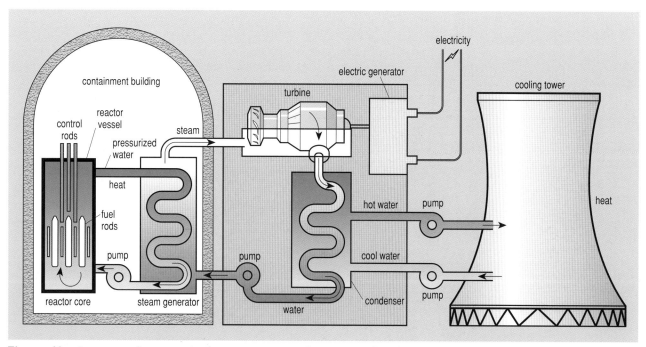

Figure 41 Anatomy of a pressurized water reactor nuclear power plant (source: Chiras, 1998, Figure 15-13, p.266)

You can find further detail of *nuclear reactor designs* in the Set Book. Whatever the design, as the fission products decay they emit electromagnetic radiation such as γ-rays and charged particles such as α- and β-particles. All these types of radiation are capable of ionizing and will therefore affect both human and other organisms and in the next section we will look at the biological effects of ionizing radiation and discuss setting limits on exposure.

Radioactivity and human health

Any radioactive material released from natural sources or artificial sources (such as nuclear reactions, nuclear weapons testing, or from artificial or natural sources) is added to the air, water or land of the biosphere. The particular radioactive chemicals can combine with one another or with other stable chemicals to form molecules that may be soluble or insoluble in water. These may be solids, liquids or gases at ordinary temperatures and pressures and can be biologically active, taking part in biochemical reactions, or be biologically inert. To us, as organisms, radioactive materials can be external to the body and emit ionizing radiation or be taken into the body with air, food, water or through the skin and then emit ionizing radiation in living cells and body tissues and organs.

If, for example, there is a nuclear accident such as a fire or explosion there will be a release of radioactive material into the atmosphere. The spread of this radioactivity and its return to the ground as radioactive fallout will depend on the initial height of the release and the weather conditions. The heaviest fragments or particles within the cloud will fall back to the ground nearest to the site of the accident whereas fine particles and gases may travel thousands of miles before being deposited. If it is raining when the cloud passes overhead a radioactive hot spot may occur many hundreds of miles from the site. Once on the ground, fallout immediately contaminates the external surfaces of grain and leafy vegetables and is also taken up internally by vegetation and animals, thereby contaminating milk and meat. People and other organisms can therefore be exposed in a number of different ways as shown in Figure 42.

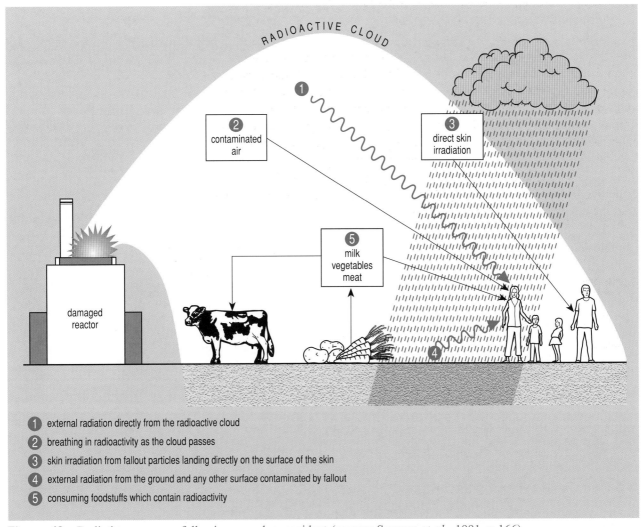

1 external radiation directly from the radioactive cloud

2 breathing in radioactivity as the cloud passes

3 skin irradiation from fallout particles landing directly on the surface of the skin

4 external radiation from the ground and any other surface contaminated by fallout

5 consuming foodstuffs which contain radioactivity

Figure 42   Radiation exposure following a nuclear accident (source: Sumner *et al.*, 1991, p.166)

Ionizing radiation in close proximity to living cells, body tissues and organs can cause damage to any part of the cell, but damage to the nucleus and particularly the DNA is likely to be the most serious.

If you are unfamiliar with the basic structure of a cell, cell division and the role of DNA take a look at Block 0: Biology, Chapter 1.

Ionizing radiation may damage the DNA in cells and prevent cell division. If the effects are confined to the individual, and not passed to their offspring, they are known as somatic effects. If the cells are part of a rapidly dividing tissue, such as the skin, the inability to detach and replace surface cells may expose more vulnerable cells underneath. Alternatively ionizing radiation may have caused a mutation in a cell which causes abnormal cell behaviour and uncontrollable cell division. Usually the body's immune system will recognize these cells as abnormal and destroy them, but sometimes this uncontrolled cell division can continue and develop into a tumour, or cancer. One cancer that is related to high levels of exposure to ionizing radiation is leukaemia (the general name given to certain cancers of the bone marrow and lymphatic system).

If damage occurs to the cells that are concerned with reproduction the gametes (sperm or ova) may be altered. This can result in a genetic defect with all the cells in the offspring's body carrying that mutation.

The amount of ionization and the amount of biological damage depends on the type of radiation. Gamma rays and other forms of electromagnetic radiation such as X-rays are photons – uncharged high-energy light waves. When emitted by a source, such as radium or cobalt, located outside the body both forms can easily pass through the body. This penetration, and particularly the different penetration by X-rays within parts of the body, can be used in diagnostic medicine to image human bones or human organs made opaque by a dye. More X-rays are absorbed, for example, by bone than by tissue and this enables the identification of different parts of the body on X-ray pictures. After an X-ray picture is taken no radiation remains in the body but any damage that has been caused by the penetration of the X-rays will remain. When X-rays or γ-rays interact with atoms they cause ionization and any biological damage is spread over several cells. In a similar way, β-particles penetrating the skin cause ionization to spread across cells, even though the β-particles do not penetrate though the whole body. In fact, β-particles only penetrate a few millimetres of metal, as shown in Figure 43.

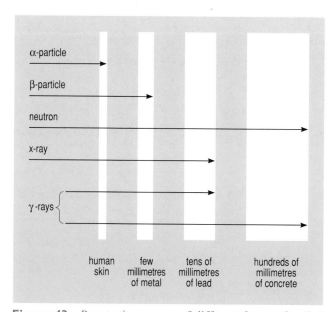

Figure 43   Penetrating power of different forms of radiation

The range of an α-particle is very short and would not penetrate much beyond the skin. Because the particle only travels a short distance the ionization is also produced locally and any biological damage is concentrated in a few cells, or even a single cell. This can make it much more difficult to repair.

Once alpha particles have entered the body they can remain near the point of entry, travel in the bloodstream or lymph fluid, or can be incorporated into particular tissues. Isotopes of plutonium, for example, have long half lives and are α-emitters. If plutonium enters the bloodstream, on average 20% may be excreted and 80% retained, mainly in the liver and skeleton.

Some isotopes may follow particular pathways in the body. For example, the isotope strontium 90 (Sr 90), which emits β-particles, is a radioactive isotope produced in the core of nuclear reactors and chemically similar to calcium. Like calcium, if Sr 90 is ingested it concentrates in the mineral part of bones.

Iodine 131 emits β-particles and γ-rays, and on entering the body it concentrates in the thyroid gland. The amount taken up by the thyroid will depend partly on the activity of the thyroid gland and also on how much non-radioactive iodine is in the body. If there is already a lot of iodine present, the radioactive iodine will have to 'compete' with the non-radioactive iodine, and less will be taken up by the thyroid. The dose and relative risk also varies with gender and with age. Estimates suggest that the relative risk for women may be greater than for men, and greater for children than for adults.

SAQ 46

Data relating to the Three Mile Island and Chernobyl nuclear accidents are given in the table below. These are the percentages of the biologically important fission products in the core of the reactors which entered the environment. (Note that in both cases the cores stayed within the containment buildings.)

Element	Percentage of total core content for the element concerned		
	Three Mile Island		*Chernobyl*
	Leaving the core	*Entering the environment*	*Entering the environment*
noble gases (Kr and Xe)	48	1	100
iodine	25	3×10^{-5}	20
caesium	53	not detected	10–13
ruthenium	0.5	not detected	3
lanthanides	nil	nil	2.5

Source: The Open University (1997), Table 6.1, p.130.

The half lives of Kr 88, Xe 133, I 131 and Cs 137 are 2.84 minutes, 5.25 days, 8.04 days and 30 years respectively.

From the information provided in Section 16.3 what safety precautions would you recommend to minimize the health effects from these two nuclear accidents?

In reality the decision to evacuate is not easy. In the case of Three Mile Island, in the end the reactor containment was not breached and in that case a mass evacuation could have increased the radiation-induced risk and non-radiation risks through traffic accidents, etc.

Countries of Europe moved quickly after Chernobyl to ban or limit imports of foodstuffs produced within about a 1000 km radius of the site. Other countermeasures included distribution of iodine tablets in Poland

and Yugoslavia, restriction of milk or dairy consumption (16 countries), banning rainwater consumption (nine countries) and restrictions of meat consumption (five countries).

16.4   Biological response to radiation

We have been looking at the potential damage to organisms and their DNA from ionizing radiation, but how do organisms respond to this damage?

Some changes to the DNA or mutations may be advantageous in certain circumstances. For example, a gene mutation or change in the DNA nucleotide sequence can slightly alter the proteins produced. This can produce an evolutionary inherited change or adaption such as a greater oxygen carrying capacity in the blood of a goat living at high altitudes, or brighter colours in the petals of a flower that must attract insects for pollination. However, most mutations caused by ionizing radiation are disadvantageous and the organism responds by trying to repair the damage. Within the nucleus new DNA may be synthesized to replace damaged strands. It is only when the level of radiation exceeds the ability of the organism to repair the damage that problems may occur. This could suggest that there may be some level of radiation where there are minimal changes and damage. However, the precise nature of this level and whether it exists at all is still a subject for debate by scientists, technologists and the nuclear industry.

To explore the debate there has to be some agreed way of measuring particular levels of radiation and estimating their effects on human health.

The quantity of energy imparted by ionizing radiation to unit mass of matter (such as tissue) is given by the SI unit called the gray, symbol Gy, where 1 Gy = 1 joule of energy absorbed from radiation by 1 kg of tissue.

But as we have already seen the biological effect of ionizing radiation will vary with the type of radiation. The biological effectiveness of particular types of radiation is called the *linear energy transfer (LET)* and is given by the following expression

LET = particle energy/track length

Radiation with the highest level of penetration or track length, such as X-rays and γ-rays, has the lowest LETs whereas α-particles have a very high LET.

SAQ 47

An α-particle and a β-particle are incident on a material and both penetrate to a depth of 2 mm. The initial energy of the β-particle is 0.5 MeV and the LET of the α-particle in this material is 10 keV μm^{-1}

(a) What is the LET for the β-particle in this medium?

(b) What is the initial energy of the α-particle?

The damage done is higher for α-particles and lower for β-particles and γ-rays, but also varies with particular cell type. To consider the whole body a quality factor (QF) is determined for each radiation type. This is defined as the ratio of the effectiveness of the radiation to the effectiveness of a reference radiation such as X-rays with an energy of 100 eV.

The biological effects of a particular radiation dose are then given as a 'dose equivalent' where

$$\text{dose equivalent} = \text{absorbed dose} \times \text{quality factor}$$

The dose equivalent is measured in the unit sievert (Sv). Thus 1 Sv corresponds to a dose of 1 Gy being given by radiation with a quality factor of 1. For β-particles, X-rays and γ-rays QF = 1, for α-particles QF = 20 and for fast neutrons QF = 10.

As we have seen, body organs also differ in their response to radiation type, for example for a particular isotope and radiation type the lungs may be more sensitive than the liver. In this case weighting factors are used to derive an effective dose equivalent also measured in sieverts. In many publications this effective dose equivalent will just be described as a dose in sieverts. For instance, on average in the UK the radiation exposure due to all sources amounts to about 2.6 mSv a year.

If you live in the UK you can look at an estimated dose at the following website: http://www.nrpb.org/understand/index.htm

Predicted effective dose equivalent values for adults for the first year after the Chernobyl accident are shown in Figure 44. This figure represents an average exposure over a year.

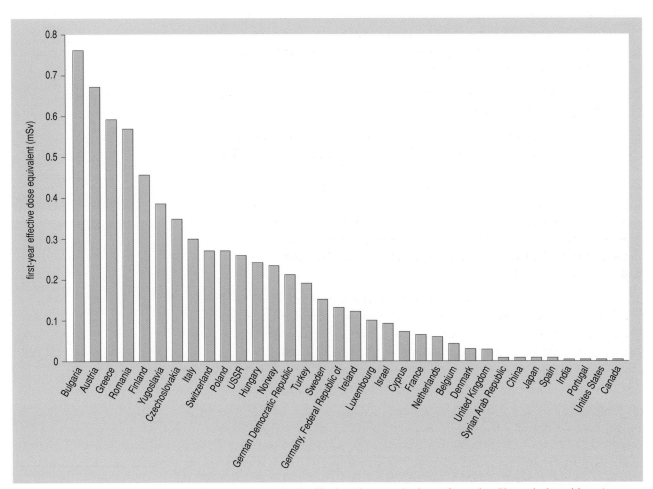

Figure 44   Country-wide average first year committed effective dose equivalents from the Chernobyl accident (source: Sumner *et al.*, 1991, p.181)

The biological damage is also influenced by the rate at which the energy is transferred or the dose rate. Any dose could be transferred in one episode over a short space of time, such as a few minutes or hours, or transferred by a succession of smaller irradiations separated by time intervals of days, weeks, months or even years. In view of this, how can we attempt to learn which effects are associated with particular dose rates and their different patterns of exposure? Where does the evidence come from?

Data on radiation hazards are regularly reviewed by two bodies – the United Nations Scientific Committee on the Effects of Atomic Radiation (UNSCEAR) and the Committee on the Biological Effects of Ionising Radiation (BEIR). Reports produced by these two bodies are reviewed by the International Commission on Radiological Protection (ICRP) who make recommendations for radiation protection. Data comes mainly from three sources:

- The survivors of the Hiroshima and Nagasaki bombings – this is the largest body of data with a total of about 100 000 people followed up for more than 40 years. Doses were acute doses of low LET radiation mostly due to external gamma rays. At these high levels observable effects begin within minutes, hours or days of the exposure. The severity of the effect increases with dose, they are fairly predictable and known as deterministic or non-stochastic effects (the word stochastic literally means random).

- Patients receiving radiotherapy – the largest group in this case was a group of 14 000 patients treated with X-rays for a spinal condition and followed up on average for 24 years.

- People who were exposed to radiation in the course of their work – the most important groups in this category are miners, particularly uranium miners. The radiation dose is due to inhaled radionuclides emitting α-particles, i.e. high LET radiation.

From these data a *dose–response* curve of excess cancer incidence against radiation dose can be constructed as shown in Figure 45.

If we were sure that the model was applicable in all cases we would be able to use it to predict excess cancers for low as well as high doses. But as you can see from Figure 45 it is not as straightforward as the dose–response curves you met earlier in Block 1. In the case of radiation there is still considerable uncertainty associated with the exact doses received and most of the data available have been for high doses and deterministic effects. So what does this mean for low doses or stochastic unpredictable random effects? What models can be used? Take another look at Figure 45 and the following text.

If we assume a straight line or linear model then no matter how small the dose it will always be associated with some increased risk of developing cancer, i.e. there will be no threshold. The alternative is a quadratic model which postulates that the additional risk of developing cancer as a result of the radiation dose is proportional to the square of the radiation dose. The response may change slowly at low doses, for example, but rapidly at high doses.

Linear dose–response
A linear dose–response is a relationship between dose and biological response that is a straight line. In other words, the rate of change (slope) in the response is the same at any dose. If Y represents the expected, or average, response and D represents dose, then a linear dose–response is written mathematically as follows

$$Y = aD$$

where a is the slope (linear coefficient).

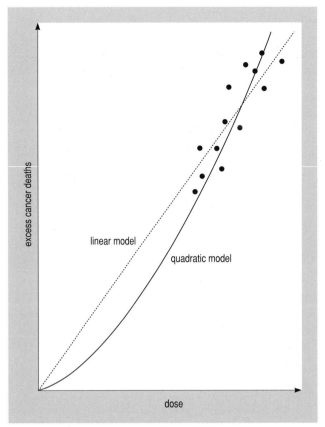

Figure 45   Dose–response curve (source: The Open University, 1997, Figure 4.6, p.77)

Linear-quadratic dose–response

A linear-quadratic dose–response is a relationship between dose and biological response that is curved. This implies that the rate of change in response is different at different doses. If Y represents the expected, or average, response and D represents dose, then a linear-quadratic dose–response is written mathematically as follows

$$Y = aD + bD^2$$

where a is the slope (linear coefficient) and b is the curvature (quadratic coefficient).

SAQ 48

(a) Explain why there is uncertainty about the form of the dose–response model at high doses.

(b) If we use a linear model rather than a linear-quadratic one will we underestimate or overestimate the risk at low doses?

SAQ 49

Using the data in the table below:

(a) calculate the number of excess cancers; and

(b) give a brief description of the relationship between dose and excess cancers.

Solid tumour cancers

Dose range (Sv)	Average dose (Sv)	Number of subjects	Number of expected background cancer deaths	Number of observed cancer deaths
0–0.009	0.004	36 132	2725.9	2562
0.01–0.05	0.02	19 518	1408.1	1394
0.06–0.09	0.07	4113	336.5	341
0.10–0.19	0.13	5209	412.6	410
0.20–0.49	0.31	6218	499.9	529
0.50–0.99	0.69	2829	214.0	273
1.0–1.99	1.36	1380	101.8	158
2.0–2.99	2.34	361	20.4	37
3.0–3.99	3.51	147	9.3	20
4.0+	4.41	84	5.5	10

Source: adapted from Shimizu *et al.* (1990).

As we have seen, there is uncertainty with the data and the models surrounding the prediction of health effects from radiation, particularly at low doses. However, international agencies and government bodies such as the ICRP and the National Radiological Protection Board (NRPB) have to take account of this uncertainty and make best estimates of risk. Based on these best estimates, the following recommended dose limits are set for the public and for radiation workers:

> public: a maximum of 1 mSv y^{-1}, averaged over five years;

> radiation workers: a maximum of 20 mSv y^{-1}, averaged over five years.

If we have some idea of limits then we can consider if we can manage radioactive waste to protect current and future generations of the human population. In the next section you can consider both the size of the problem of radioactive waste and some of the strategies that have been suggested and used.

16.5 Radioactive waste management

What is radioactive waste? The International Atomic Energy Authority (IAEA) defines radioactive waste as 'any material that contains a concentration of radionuclides greater than those deemed safe by national authorities and for which no use is foreseen'.

Compare this definition with the definitions of waste discussed at the beginning of this block.

As we discussed earlier, this waste can arise from natural sources with radioisotopes such as potassium in food, radium and uranium in rocks, and artificial sources such as those used in medicine and those arising from nuclear power and nuclear weapons. Take a look at Figure 46, which gives an outline of the wastes produced from a typical nuclear power station.

In the following section we will consider the size of both natural and artificial sources, the implications for defining the scope of any regulatory system and waste classification. Finally you will be introduced to some of the disposal options and plans for the future.

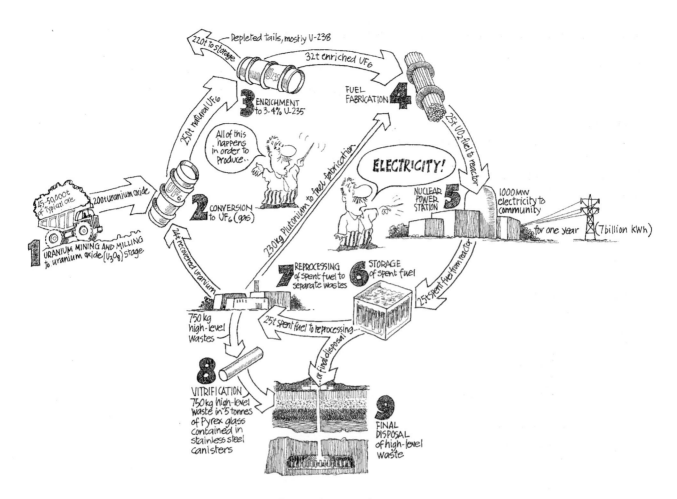

Figure 46 The nuclear fuel cycle (source: http//www.uic.com.au)

16.5.1 Sources of radioactivity

The world inventory of radioactive material is largely unknown so it is very difficult to provide global estimates that are meaningful. However, the following examples should give you some sense of the scale of estimated doses from natural and artificial sources.

The unit Becquerel is a measure of the number of disintegrations within a radionuclide, where 1 Bq = 1 disintegration per second.

Everyone is exposed to natural radiation. The natural sources include cosmic rays and naturally occurring radioactive substances existing in the Earth itself and inside the human body. Table 25 gives a summary of the average worldwide exposure to natural radiation sources and you can see that the most significant contribution is due to radon gas, which emanates from the soil and may concentrate in houses. (See http://www.nrpb.org/understand/index.htm for further discussion and a map of the radon areas in England.)

Natural processes such as volcanic eruptions, mineral water springs, erosion and movements of sands can play an important part in increasing exposure levels. For example, the natural radioactivity in the sea is estimated to be of the order of 10 000 exabequerel (EBq) (IAEA, 2000). In natural waters, such as those surrounding the Caspian Sea, spring waters rich in radium 226 emerge and deposit tailings of precipitates as shown in Figure 47.

Note: 1 EBq = 10^{18} Bq.

Table 25 Average worldwide exposure to natural radiation sources

Source of exposure	Annual effective dose (mSv)	
	Average	*Typical range*
Cosmic radiation		
Directly ionizing and photon component	0.28	0.3–1.0
Neutron component	0.10	
Cosmogenic radionuclides	0.01	
Total cosmic and cosmogenic	0.39	
External terrestrial radiation		
Outdoors	0.07	0.3–0.6
Indoors	0.14	
Total external terrestrial radiation	0.48	
Inhalation exposure		
Uranium and thorium series	0.006	0.2–10
Radon (^{222}Rn)	1.15	
Thoron (^{220}Rn)	0.10	
Total inhalation exposure	1.26	
Ingestion exposure		
^{40}K	0.17	0.2–0.8
Uranium and thorium series	0.12	
Total ingestion exposure	0.29	
Total	2.4	1–10

Source: adapted from UNSCEAR (2000).

Figure 47 Deposits of radium 226 in the waters surrounding the Caspian Sea (source: IAEA, 2000)

These tailings have radioactivity levels that can deliver high radiation exposures to residents which are up to 100 times more than the international exposure limit applicable to radioactive waste disposal of 1 mSv per year. Similarly, monazite, sand in coastal areas such as Rio de Janeiro and Espirito Santo in Brazil can deliver exposures that are on average 3.6 times higher than the international limit.

Industries such as mining and industrial processes such as phosphorus production, primary iron and steel production and cement production can all use naturally occurring radioactive materials (generally referred to as NORMs). The concentration of the radioactive material in the product and the waste can be much higher than in the ore. For example, in the areas of Chkalovsk and Taborsha in Tajikistan, residual waste tailings from past mining and milling operations have been estimated to be around 50 million tonnes, with a total amount of radioactivity of up to 0.001 EBq. Similar tailings exist in many other parts of the world.

Public concern about radioactivity usually focuses on artificial sources from nuclear weapons, nuclear power and medicine. The production of nuclear materials for military purposes has left a legacy of large amounts of radioactive residues in some parts of the world. In the USA, the management of radioactive wastes from defence activities involves:

- remediating nearly 10 trillion litres of contaminated groundwater, an amount equal to approximately four times the daily US water consumption;

- remediating 40 million cubic metres of contaminated soil and debris, enough to fill approximately 17 professional sports stadiums;

- safely storing and guarding more than 18 tonnes of weapons-usable plutonium, enough for thousands of nuclear weapons;

- managing over 2000 tonnes of intensely radioactive spent nuclear fuel;

- storing, treating and disposing of radioactive and hazardous waste, including over 160 000 cubic metres that are currently in storage and over half a billion litres of liquid, high-level radioactive waste;

- deactivating and/or decommissioning about 4000 facilities that are no longer needed to support active missions;

- implementing critical nuclear non-proliferation programmes for accepting and safely managing spent nuclear fuel from foreign research reactors that contain weapons-usable highly enriched uranium; and

- providing long-term care and monitoring – or stewardship – for potentially hundreds of years at an estimated 109 sites following clean-up.

Table 26 gives the amounts of radioactive waste and spent fuel accumulated in the Russian Federation.

Table 26 Amounts of accumulated radioactive waste and spent fuel in the Russian Federation

Ministries, departments and organizations	Responsibilities	Liquids		Solids		Spent fuel	
		m^3	Bq	m^3	Bq	$Tons$	Bq
Ministry of the Russian Federation for Atomic Energy (Minatom)	Uranium ore mining and processing, uranium enrichment, nuclear fuel manufacturing, nuclear power production, spent fuel reprocessing and nuclear weapon materials production	4.0×10^8	6.3×10^{19}	2.2×10^8	8.14×10^{18}	8700	17.02×10^{19}
Ministry of Defence of the Russian Federation (Navy)	Operation and utilization of nuclear ships and submarines	1.4×10^4	4.44×10^{12}	1.3×10^4	29.6×10^{12}	30	5.55×10^{17}
Ministry of Economy of the Russian Federation Department of Defence Industry	Construction, repair and utilization of nuclear ships and submarines	3.2×10^3	18.5×10^{10}	1.5×10^3	3.7×10^{12}	a	a
Ministry of Transport of the Russian Federation	Operation and utilization of nuclear icebreakers	4.4×10^2	5.5×10^{13}	7.3×10^2	3.7×10^{16}	10	17.39×10^{17}
Radon Special Enterprises	Processing and disposal of radioactive materials, used in medicine, scientific research, industry, etc.	—	—	2.0×10^5	7.77×10^{16}	—	—
Totals		4.0×10^8	6.29×10^{19}	2.2×10^8	8.5×10^{18}	8740	17.39×10^{19}

[a] More than 100 nuclear-powered submarines and their spent fuel are awaiting decommissioning.

Collective dose is the quantity obtained by multiplying the average dose by the number of people exposed to a given source of ionizing radiation.

The waste from peaceful use of nuclear energy may amount to approximately 1000 EBq for all the nuclear power production around the world, and is estimated to be growing at approximately 100 EBq per year. With a present world nuclear energy generation of 250 GW, the *collective dose* per year of practice is estimated to be 200 man Sv. If the practice of nuclear power production is limited to the next 100 years at the present capacity the maximum effective dose per head to the global population is less than 0.2 μSv and very small compared with natural background levels. Similarly, estimates of releases of isotopes produced and used in industrial and medical applications are associated with low levels of exposure. The highest exposures, averaging about 0.5 mSv, may be received by family members of patients who have received iodine 131 therapeutic treatments.

The collective dose is the quantity obtained by multiplying the average dose by the number of people exposed to a given source of ionizing radiation.

For the UK, the high contribution of natural radiation is further illustrated in Figure 48.

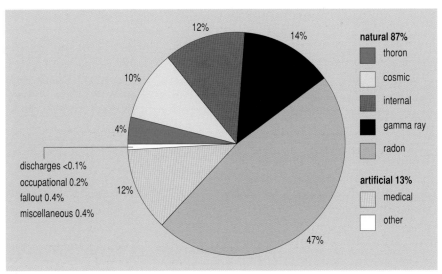

Figure 48   Composition of total radiation exposure in the UK (source: DoE, undated)

SAQ 50

Nuclear power plants produce practically no carbon dioxide emissions. Explain why this could be used to justify an expansion of nuclear power.

It is worth bearing in mind the information and uncertainties associated with the pie chart in Figure 48. An environmental model is needed to estimate the amount of a radioactive substance to which people are exposed. A biological model is used to estimate the radiation doses which will arise from exposure to the estimated amount of radioactivity including the use of a quality factor and weighting for different organs. The resulting doses are then averaged over the whole UK population, which means that relatively high doses for people living near Sellafield, for example, are diluted by much greater numbers receiving low doses.

With this uncertainty for both natural and artificial sources of radioactivity, how do we aim to protect the public? Should radiation protection regulations be applied to everything, to every human activity, to every environmental situation and to every waste?

In reality, regulatory systems only have limited resources and capabilities. The ICRP and the IAEA have limited the scope of their system through the use of International Basic Safety Standards for Protection against Ionizing Radiation and for the Safety of Radiation Sources. In these standards the concept of exclusion is used to remove certain exposures from the regulations, particularly those that cannot be controlled or are difficult to control, e.g. exposure to cosmic rays. The inhabitants of La Paz in Bolivia, located at an altitude of 4000 m, incur higher exposures than people living at sea level, yet it is not possible to move the city to a lower altitude. Other areas of exclusion currently include 'unmodified radionuclides in most raw materials'.

This seems to be a reasonable approach for situations that are not feasible to regulate but there may well be some industries using NORMs where radioactivity concentrations and resultant exposures are high enough to warrant consideration and control. Some of these exposures from natural wastes are being suggested for inclusion within the scope of the regulations.

Whether the radioactive waste is derived from natural or artificial sources the form of the source and type of radiation may vary as well as the activity level and the heat content. To facilitate the exchange of information and practice between countries disposing of waste the IAEA has derived a waste classification system that will be described in the next section.

16.5.2 Levels of waste

In 1994 the IAEA revised the waste classification system to include three principal classes: exempt waste (EW), low and intermediate level waste (LILW), and high level waste (HLW).

Waste that is classified as LILW and HLW needs to be managed. Managing radioactive waste involves a sequence of operations which includes waste generation, storage (including temporary retention of waste), transport and disposal. Disposal means the discarding of waste with no intention of retrieval. For nuclear power, the operations start with the management of spent fuel from nuclear reactors and ends with the safe disposal of the unusable radioactive substances. The primary objective of all radioactive waste management is to protect people and the environment from hazards arising from waste and effluents, both now and in the future.

Exempt waste
Exempt waste contains such a low concentration of radionuclides that it can be excluded from nuclear regulatory control because radiological hazards are considered negligible. This principle was converted into an annual dose of around 10 μSv, which is equivalent to less than 1% of the average natural background level.

Low and intermediate level waste
Low and intermediate level waste contains enough radioactive material to require actions to ensure the protection of workers and the public for short or extended periods of time. This class includes a range of materials, from just above exempt levels to those with sufficiently high levels of radioactivity to require use of shielding containers, and in some cases periods for cooling off. LILW may be subdivided into categories according to the half lives of the radionuclides it contains, with 'short-lived' being less than 30 years and 'long-lived' greater than 30 years.

Low level waste arises, mainly as lightly contaminated miscellaneous scrap, wherever radioactive materials are used. The major components are metals in the form of redundant equipment and organic materials in the form of discarded protective clothing, paper towels and plastic wrapping. In the UK, waste in this category should not exceed 4 GBq t^{-1} of α- or 12 GBq^{-1} of β- or γ-activity.

Intermediate level waste arises mainly from the dismantling and reprocessing of spent nuclear fuel and from general operations and maintenance of radioactive plant. The major components are metals, with smaller quantities of inorganic flocs and sludges, organic materials, cement and graphite. In this category the radioactivity levels exceed the upper boundaries for low level wastes but do not require heating to be taken into account in the design of storage or disposal facilities.

In the UK anyone who wishes to accumulate or dispose of radioactive waste must obtain prior written agreement (an 'Authorization') from the Environment Agency (or the appropriate national regulator). The management of radioactive waste on nuclear licensed sites is regulated by the Health and Safety Executive (HSE) through the Nuclear Installations Inspectorate (NII).

High level waste

High level waste contains sufficiently high levels of radioactive materials that a high degree of isolation from the biosphere, normally in a geological repository, is required for long periods of time. The temperature in these wastes may rise significantly as a result of their radioactivity, so this has to be taken into account in designing storage or disposal facilities. Such wastes normally require both special shielding and cooling off periods.

Spent fuel from commercial, research reactors and military reactors is classified as HLW. Some countries regard it as an asset because usable material can be reprocessed into new reactor fuel. The IAEA estimates that about 10 000 tonnes of spent fuel are discharged every year by the world's 433 operating nuclear power plants. Over the past four decades, the cumulative amount of spent fuel discharged worldwide was about 220 000 tonnes by the end of 1999. About 145 000 tonnes were in storage facilities, while about 75 000 tonnes were reprocessed. By the year 2015 the cumulative amount of spent fuel is projected to surpass 390 000 tonnes as shown in Figure 49.

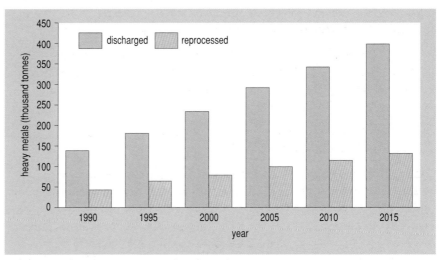

Figure 49   Projected spent fuel trends (source: IAEA, 2000, p.11)

SAQ 51

This question concerns the handling and disposal of the iodine isotope $^{131}_{53}I$ which decays by β-emission and has a half life of 8 days. You may assume that the energy of the β-particle is 0.6 MeV and the energy of the accompanying γ-ray is 0.4 MeV. The iodine is delivered as the compound potassium iodide (KI) which has a solubility in water of 1.28 kg l^{-1}. The LET for both types of radiation in water is 1 keV μm^{-1}.

Suppose that the isotope is to be used for the treatment of patients in a National Health Service hospital. The potassium iodide (1 kg) is delivered on Day 1 and the activity is measured as 1 MBq. It is immediately dissolved in water to produce 1 litre of solution. The flask containing this solution is sealed and is stored in a large water bath.

(a) What is the radiation product formed as the iodine decays?

(b) Calculate the activity of the solution on Day 2.

(c) On Day 2, 30 ml of this solution is removed from the flask and diluted with further water so that the final solution has an activity of 10 000 Bq l^{-1}. How much water has to be added to produce this solution?

(d) 30% of this solution is used to treat a patient and it may be assumed that it is all ingested by the patient. At the end of the day only 200 ml of solution are left in the flask.

   (i) Calculate the amount of radioactivity that is unaccounted for.

   (ii) What is the activity of the residual solution?

16.5.3   Disposal methods

Three general principles are employed in the management of radioactive wastes:

■ concentrate and contain;

■ dilute and disperse;

■ delay and decay.

Short-lived LILW from nuclear power plants, research reactors, medical and industrial activities is often treated (to achieve volume reduction) and/ or conditioned (waste immobilization) prior to disposal. Treatment options include chemical precipitation, incineration and compaction followed by immobilization in materials such as concrete, bitumen or polymers.

Treated and conditioned wastes are typically disposed of in shallow concrete-lined trenches or engineered surface structures. The isolation period is usually up to 300 years, with associated administrative and institutional control of the site.

More than 100 of these shallow facilities have been built and more than 30 are under development worldwide.

In the UK, intermediate level waste generation is predicted to continue at the current rate of about 3000 cubic metres a year until 2010 and then exhibit a lower and reducing rate as nuclear power stations are shut down, spent fuel reprocessing ceases and the scale of other operations is reduced. Similarly, low level wastes are predicted to continue to be produced at their current rate of about 10 000 cubic metres a year until 2010, and then to fall steadily until 2050.

Some long-lived LILW contains radionuclides in quantities that require a high degree of isolation from the biosphere. This is typically provided by disposal in geological formations, such as ancient salt domes or granite tunnels, at depths of several hundred metres.

High level waste needs safe isolation well beyond the life-spans of current or forthcoming generations. The objective is to isolate the waste from the biosphere for extremely long periods of time. Any residual radioactive substances reaching the biosphere should be at concentrations that are insignificant compared with the natural background levels of radioactivity, and any risk from inadvertent human intrusion would have to be very small.

Although progress is being made, and many countries are planning geological disposal for long-lived LILW and HLW, there are as yet no operating sites in any country. However, in May 2001, Finland became the first country to approve plans for a geological repository for HLW. The Finnish waste-disposal company Posiva Oy will research possible sites and plans to start building the repository in 2010.

The USA's Waste Isolation Pilot Plant (WIPP) is located 700 metres deep in a salt formation. The site is the world's first geological repository and has been approved for receiving US defence-related long-lived wastes, but not HLW.

There have also been developments at Yucca Mountain in Nevada. The US President George Bush signed a resolution in July 2002 approving Yucca Mountain as a national repository for spent fuel and high level radioactive waste. This enables the Department of Energy (DoE) to prepare and submit a licence application to the Nuclear Regulatory Commission (NRC), which is scheduled for late 2004.

Disposal of spent fuel is, however, still an issue that needs resolving. Although there are some promising developments in reprocessing which could considerably reduce the volume, and convert the waste into vitrified solid HLW, there are still concerns. For projected reactor requirements sufficient containment storage is planned, but there are some countries where storage sites are nearing full capacity. And there are still ethical questions surrounding geological disposal which have yet to be addressed. Should the current generation attempt to dispose of HLW in a way that requires no action in the future? or should the waste be stored in a retrievable way for future generations of technologists?

SAQ 52

Explain briefly why there may be concerns about an expansion of nuclear power in the UK.

16.6   Summary

There are natural and artificial sources of radioactivity. Nuclear processes such as fusion and fission change atomic nuclei and release large amounts of energy – measured in electronvolts (eV). Unstable nuclei undergo exponential radioactive decay and produce α-, β- and γ-radiation. All these forms of radiation are capable of removing one or more electrons from an atom and causing ionization. The time for half of a particular nuclei in a sample to decay is called the half life, $t_{1/2}$.

Any radioactive material is added to the biosphere. People can be exposed directly from external radiation, or indirectly by inhalation or ingestion of radioactive material. The type of ionizing radiation will influence the amount of ionization and the biological effectiveness or linear energy transfer (LET). X-rays and γ-rays have the highest penetration and the lowest LETs whereas α- and β-radiation have high LETs.

Damage from ionizing radiation can prevent cell division and cause mutations and cancer. Body organs differ in their response to different radiation types and the whole body dose is calculated using Quality Factors to give a dose equivalent. Predicting excess cancers from particular doses of radiation is uncertain and the data are incomplete, especially for low doses.

Artificial sources of radiation, such as nuclear weapons and nuclear power, represent less than 0.3% of the average global exposure. To control waste and protect the public, standards are used and waste is classified into three main categories – exempt waste, low and intermediate level waste and high level waste. The management of waste is still not resolved and is usually one of containment and isolation to prevent any residual radioactivity from reaching the biosphere.

17 CONTAMINATED LAND

Someone with money to invest was once given the following advice:

Buy land, they aren't making any more of it.

Until relatively recently this view was not widely held and land was treated as though it was an inexhaustible resource. In the UK, with its legacy of land contaminated by the industrial activities of previous generations, the attitude was that contaminated land could be ignored and industry, commerce and housing could always be developed on greenfield sites. Pressure to find land for these activities is now increasing and the Government has set the target that 60% of all new houses should be built on 'brownfield' sites to relieve the pressure on greenfield sites and preserve the countryside. Not all brownfield sites are contaminated, but many of them are. Therefore there is a need to implement programmes to decontaminate such land so it can be brought back into use.

Furthermore, contaminated land can present a health risk through a number of processes. Food crops growing in contaminated soils can bioaccumulate *heavy metals* such as lead and cadmium. Also, contaminated soil particles adhering to food crops may be ingested if the crops are not washed fully. Children playing on contaminated land can also ingest potentially toxic elements (PTEs) and other pollutants. PTEs is a term that includes the heavy metals and also some non-metals such as arsenic.

Tars, oils and other corrosive substances can cause skin irritation and burns through direct contact with soils contaminated with these substances.

Liquid contaminants (such as organic solvents) can leach through the soils and contaminate aquifers and surface waters. There is a particular danger of this happening when sites are disturbed during demolition or construction work.

Contamination can occur due to the presence of flammable substances such as coal, coke, oils, landfill gas and landfilled municipal and industrial wastes. If these substances are heated – perhaps by contact with buried power cables, the careless disposal of hot ashes or from surface fires, they may ignite and continue to burn beneath the ground. Underground fires are particularly difficult to extinguish and can lead to the release of toxic gases and additional contamination through the release of liquids containing organic compounds into the ground and possibly into watercourses.

Many essential plant nutrients (for example, boron, copper, nickel and zinc) inhibit or even prevent the growth of plants if present in high concentrations in the soil. Methane and other toxic gases can also cause phytotoxic effects by depleting the oxygen content of soil in the root zone.

Finally, several contaminants may attack concrete, metals and plastics in building foundations and pipework. These include acids, oils, tarry substances and organic solvents.

For both health and land-use reasons the Government implemented its statutory regime for identifying and treating contaminated land in England in April 2000. (Similar regimes exist in the rest of the UK.) At the same time, the Environment Minister wrote to the chairmen of the UK's top 350 companies asking them to prepare plans to identify and restore any contaminated land on sites that they owned.

17.1   Regulation

Under the Contaminated Land (England) Regulations introduced in 2000, the district, borough or unitary local authority is principally responsible for implementing the regulations. For sites that could potentially have a significant effect on drinking water, surface waters or aquifers the Environment Agency becomes the responsible body. The Agency is also responsible for particular industrial, nuclear or military sites.

Under the Regulations, land is classed as contaminated when it contains or overlies substances that are causing significant harm or pollution of controlled waters. Land is also classed as contaminated if there is a significant possibility of harm or water pollution being caused.

Local authorities are responsible for:

- identifying any sites in their area which may be contaminated;

- determining whether the site is contaminated;

- deciding what remediation is necessary and ensuring that it is carried out;

- maintaining a register (available to the public) of contaminated sites and remedial actions taken.

The Environment Agency will assist the local authorities in the first three of these tasks through the provision of guidance documents and providing site-specific help when required.

The cost of carrying out remediation work will be met by the body that caused or allowed the contamination to take place. If this body cannot be identified the costs will be met by the current owner of the land (unless the problem is solely one of water pollution). If neither of these bodies can be identified the costs are met by the local authority and support from central government is available.

17.2   Quantities of contaminated land and types of contamination

Contamination can occur through several routes. Accidental spillage of hazardous substances, uncontrolled disposal of wastes, and leakage from storage tanks and pipework are the most common. In recent years leaks from underground fuel storage tanks and pipes have been a major source, which accounts for the number of contaminated petrol stations and garages. There are also thousands of sites which have been contaminated by previous industrial use, often associated with manufacturing processes that are now obsolete such as gasworks and metal refining plants.

A survey undertaken for the former Department of the Environment, Transport and the Regions suggested that over 320 000 hectares are affected in Great Britain and that the total cost of clean-up may be around £15.2 billion. In terms of the number of sites, petrol stations, engineering works, coal preparation plants and waste management sites are the most significant, whilst the most significant in terms of area of land are sewage works, engineering works and coal preparation plants, (Table 27). Contamination can be caused by several types of material, and the main contaminants and their potential sources are shown in Table 28.

Table 27   Contaminated land in Great Britain

Sector	Number of sites	Total area (ha)
Petrol stations and garages	120 000	8000
Engineering works	43 305	49 390
Coal preparation plants	1800	31 500
Waste treatment and disposal sites (including landfills)	5500	25 000
Gasworks	2000	6940
Oil refineries	40	12 000
Sewage works	800	100 000
Railway land	175	17 500
Airfields	1370	27 400
Primary iron and steel manufacture	300	13 350
Chemical works	4185	7462
Printing works	10 000	2240
Scrap yards	12 000	1690
Textile and dye works	11 200	5440
Road transport centres	800	4300
Docks	500	9500
Total	213 975	321 712

Source: ENDS (2000).

Table 28   Commonly encountered contaminants

Contaminant	Likely sources	Principal hazard
'Potentially toxic elements' (cadmium, lead, arsenic, mercury)	Metal mines; iron and steel works; foundries; smelters	Harmful to human and animal health if ingested directly or indirectly
Other metals (copper, nickel, zinc)	Electroplating, anodizing and galvanizing works; engineering works; scrap yards and ship-breaking yards	May restrict or prevent plant growth
Combustible substances (coal and coke dust, oil)	Gasworks; power stations; railway land; petrol stations	Underground fires
Flammable gases (methane)	Landfill sites; filled dock basins	Explosions within or beneath buildings
'Aggressive substances' (sulphates, chlorides, acids)	Chemical works; metal treatment plants; 'made ground', including slag from blast furnaces	Chemical attack on building materials
Oily and tarry substances (oil, phenols)	Chemical works; refineries; by-product plants; tar distilleries; petrol stations and garages	Contamination of water supplies by deterioration of service mains; groundwater and aquifer pollution
Asbestos	Industrial buildings; waste disposal sites	Cancer risk if inhaled

Compare the contaminants in Table 28 with the hazardous properties shown in the box in Section 5.2. Draw up a table showing which contaminants may be classed as hazardous wastes and why.

17.3   Assessing contaminated land

The broad definition of contaminated land is given in the Environmental Protection Act of 1990 which states that contaminated land is:

> 'any land which appears to the local authority in whose area it is situated to be in such a condition, by reason of substances in, on or under the land, that:

> ■ Significant harm is being caused or there is a significant possibility of such harm being caused; or

> ■ Pollution of controlled waters is being, or is likely to be caused.'

For land to be classed as contaminated three features need to be present.

1   A source of contamination that has the potential to cause harm to human health or pollute controlled waters.

2   A pathway (or pathways) that allow the contaminant to come into contact with people or controlled waters.

3   A receptor that can be affected by the contamination. The receptor can be a living organism, an ecological system or a piece of property.

This means that land can be 'polluted' but not 'contaminated' if there is either no receptor present or no pathway to link the source and the receptor. For example, the soil below a car park may contain high levels of a particular heavy metal, but if the car park is built on a concrete pad, the soil is above the water table and it overlies a layer of impermeable clay, there is no pathway to link the metal to the wider environment. Therefore, the land would not be classed as contaminated.

Guidance has been developed for the assessment of contaminated land by Defra, the Environment Agency and the Scottish Environment Protection Agency. This guidance is in the form of the CLEA (Contaminated Land Exposure Assessment) model which allows users to determine whether a particular site needs to be remediated and the form this remediation should take (Environment Agency, 2006).

The CLEA model and associated guidance assists assessors through the processes of undertaking a risk assessment, appraising the options for remediation and implementing a remediation strategy. To assist with the process a series of 'soil guideline values' (SGVs) has been set. SGVs are based on human toxicity data and estimates of human intake from soil exposure. They are 'intervention values' and indicate that concentrations above the values could pose an unacceptable health risk. If a local authority or landowner finds levels above the SGVs, further investigation (and possibly remediation) should be undertaken. A sample of SGVs is shown in Table 29.

Table 29   Soil Guideline Values

Contaminant	SGV (mg kg^{-1})			
	Residential land where plant uptake is possible	Residential land where plant uptake is not possible	Allotments	Commercial/ industrial land
Lead	450	450	450	750
Selenium	35	260	35	8000
Nickel	50	75	50	5000
Mercury	8	15	8	480
Chromium	130	200	130	5000
Cadmium at all pH values	-	30	-	1400
Cadmium				
pH 6	1	-	1	-
pH 7	2	-	2	-
pH 8	8	-	8	-
Arsenic	20	20	20	500
Phenol at soil organic matter of:				
1%	78	21 900	80	21 900
2.5%	150	34 400	155	43 000
5%	280	37 300	280	78 100

Note that 'residential with plant uptake' is used for developments with individual gardens and 'residential without plant uptake' for developments with communal gardens or no gardens.

17.4   Treatment methods

Dilution
One of the simplest methods of dealing with contaminated land is to import additional uncontaminated material onto the site and mix it with the contaminated soil in sufficient quantities to reduce contaminant levels to below the trigger concentration. This avoids the need for any other treatment.

Excavation and landfill
Another simple way of dealing with contaminated soil is to remove it from the site for disposal in a landfill site. Depending on the degree of contamination this may require a landfill licensed to take special wastes. For less contaminated soils, a non-inert site will be acceptable. This technique is widely used in the UK; it is reliable and cheap if a local site can be found. On the other hand, this does not solve the problem, but merely relocates the contamination.

Containment and encapsulation
Containment is a method of treating moderately contaminated soils. After removing any pockets of heavy contamination the remaining contaminated material is covered with layers of clay followed by topsoil or hardstanding

to provide a physical barrier between users and the contamination. Synthetic membranes can be used in place of the clay.

Encapsulation is a variation on containment whereby horizontal and vertical barriers are used to surround the contamination from the sides, top and bottom.

Physical treatment

In this method, physical processes are used to remove contaminants. A number of processes can be used; some of them are carried out in situ and do not involve large-scale excavation work, while other processes are carried out on excavated soil (ex situ). Ex situ processes tend to separate the soil into an uncontaminated fraction and a much smaller, but highly contaminated fraction which is removed from the site for treatment or disposal.

The main in situ methods are venting and vacuum extraction. Venting is often used to treat landfills, producing small amounts of landfill gas, and other sites where organic material may be degrading. A series of wells is sunk and the gas migrates to the wells and is vented to the atmosphere. Vacuum extraction is based on this method and used to treat land contaminated by volatile organic compounds such as solvents. A system of wells is sunk in the contaminated area and linked to a vacuum pump. Under the action of the vacuum, volatile and semi-volatile pollutants are drawn through the soil and out of the wells. The contaminated air is then either passed through an absorption column or treated in a small incinerator.

Ex situ methods rely on the fact that contaminants tend to be associated with the smaller soil particles (silts and clays) owing to their high surface to volume ratio and the effect of surface attractive forces. This principle applies to many contaminants including heavy metals, hydrocarbons and organo-chlorine compounds. Washing the soil by passing it through a system of hydrocyclones (cyclones that use water rather than air as the carrying fluid) can result in a decontaminated product containing 70–90% of the original mass and a contaminated residue containing 10–30% of the original mass.

Ex situ separation can be achieved by other processes that exploit the different physical properties of the fine and coarse fractions. These processes are based on standard mineral processing operations such as screening and froth flotation.

Solidification/stabilization

Solidification processes aim to minimize the spread of pollution by converting the contaminated material into a solid impermeable mass with a low surface to volume ratio. This is often achieved by adding a binder such as cement or quicklime to the soil.

Stabilization is a form of solidification where reagents are added which convert the contamination to a less-soluble form by chemical reaction or pH adjustment.

Thermal treatment

Thermal processes include direct heating, indirect heating and incineration. Direct and indirect heating are used to volatilize organic compounds in the soil which can then be removed by other methods (such as air stripping) for subsequent treatment by absorption or incineration. Incineration is an ex situ process where the soil is burned in a rotary kiln incinerator (see Section 15.2). The end product contains no organic material and can no longer be considered to be a soil.

Solvent extraction

Solvent extraction is an ex situ method that is effective in treating soils contaminated with toxic organic compounds such as herbicides, pesticides, polynuclear aromatic hydrocarbons (PAHs) and polychlorinated biphenyls (PCBs). The excavated soil is mixed with a solvent (such as triethylamine) and held in suspension in a reactor to allow the contaminants to migrate to the solvent. The suspension is then separated by gravity settling or centrifuging and the soil is returned to the site after drying. The solvent is then recovered for reuse and the organic contaminants are incinerated.

Chemical treatment

Chemical treatment is an extension of stabilization in which the contaminants are either destroyed or converted to a less environmentally damaging form using in situ processes. These processes include oxidation, reduction and hydrolysis. A disadvantage of these processes is that reactions can also occur with the soil materials and these may either damage the soil structure or generate new toxic compounds.

Bioremediation

Biodegradable pollutants present can often be treated in situ using micro-organisms. Conditions within the site are modified so as to encourage native microbes already present to biodegrade the pollutants. While native microbes adapted to the environment are usually preferred, 'tailor made' species effective in decomposing a particular pollutant may sometimes be added to the soil.

Microbial activity is enhanced by the supply of nutrients such as oxygen, N, P and trace elements. Oxygen may be supplied in a variety of ways – as air, pure oxygen, hydrogen peroxide, ozone or nitrate. Very often the groundwater at the site is pumped out and used as the transport medium for the nutrients. The nutrients are added to the abstracted groundwater which is then sent back into the ground through infiltration trenches. In many instances the groundwater is itself polluted with the hazardous waste and requires treatment first.

Figure 50 shows a possible treatment scheme for a site contaminated by fuel which has leaked from an underground storage tank. Groundwater is drawn out through two extraction wells and passed to a skimmer tank where free oil rises to the surface and is separated. In the following stage an air stripper removes volatile organic components from the groundwater. The separated volatile components are then degraded in a compost filter or may be adsorbed onto activated carbon (if this is not done the pollutants will merely be transferred from the water phase into the air). After this stage, nutrients needed for essential degradation are added and the water is put back into the ground via infiltration trenches. As the water percolates through the ground it takes with it the nutrients to the points at which the waste is located. The microbes present at these points utilize the nutrients in biodegrading the waste.

Bioremediation in situ is gaining popularity as a means of treating biodegradable hazardous waste. It eliminates the need for excavation and transportation of contaminated soil, which is a costly and disruptive operation. It also allows the treatment of both soil and groundwater. It has minimal equipment requirements and has generally been cost-effective as a means of treating hazardous wastes.

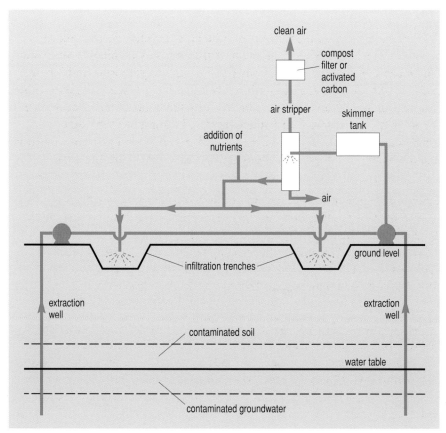

Figure 50 A possible treatment scheme for a site contaminated by fuel oil

17.5   Treatment in the UK

As we will see below, UK land remediation projects have generally used landfill or containment techniques, but many technologies have received waste management licences in England and Wales. These technologies include bioremediation, soil vapour extraction, soil washing, solvent extraction and solidification.

In 1997, the Environment Agency set a target that 50% of the total land remediation projects would use sustainable methods by 2001/02. A survey carried out by Birmingham University in 1999 reported that the following techniques were used in a sample of sites treated by either the local authority or the site's owner (Table 30).

Table 30   UK soil remediation techniques

Excavation and landfill	76%
Containment by a geotechnical cap	17%
Containment by building or hardstanding	9%
Excavation and on-site disposal	8%
Vacuum extraction	9%
Soil vapour extraction	2.7%
Ex situ bioremediation	3%
Ex situ soil washing	2%

Source: Environment Agency (1999).

SAQ 54

Which of the techniques for treating contaminated land in Section 17.4 would you regard as being 'sustainable'?

17.6   Scale of operation and cost

A smaller sample of the authorities and companies involved in the Birmingham University survey reported on the cost and scale of their remediation projects. A quarter of the projects cost less than £50 000 and around two-thirds cost less than £500 000. At the other extreme, three of the projects cost over £13 million with the Millennium Dome remediation site costs amounting to £147 million.

The cost of these projects is summarized by volume of material processed in Figure 51. While these sums are not generally excessive, it is important to bear in mind that there are around 214 000 contaminated sites in Britain. Many of these will require treatment if the land is to be redeveloped.

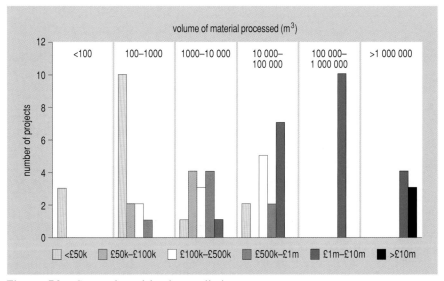

Figure 51   Contaminated land remediation costs

17.7   Summary

Contaminated land is land that has become polluted due to its previous industrial use and has the potential for harming human health or the environment. Contamination is due to a number of pollutants such as potentially toxic elements (PTEs), fuels, corrosive/caustic materials, oils/tars and asbestos.

It is estimated that there are about 320 000 hectares of contaminated land in England. In terms of numbers, former garages and petrol stations account for the highest proportion, but by area, sewage works and engineering works account for the largest proportion.

There are several ways of treating contaminated land. The simplest methods are taking the contaminated soil for landfill disposal or using engineering solutions to isolate it from the environment. More sustainable methods include extracting organic contaminants by vacuum, soil washing (to concentrate the pollutants in a relatively small fraction of the original material) and bio-remediation, whereby micro-organisms are used to break down organic contaminants.

ANSWERS TO SELF-ASSESSMENT QUESTIONS

SAQ 1

My list included:

- vegetable peelings;
- plate scrapings;
- meat trimmings;
- grass cuttings;
- weeds;

- leaflets;
- old catalogues;
- draft printing;
- dust; and
- dead flowers.

SAQ 2

The two strategies propose similar recycling and recovery rates for 2010 with the English strategy setting higher targets. However, the English figures refer to municipal waste while Northern Ireland limits them to household waste. Direct comparisons are therefore difficult to make, but the important point is that both sets of targets will require a major change in the way that wastes are managed.

Northern Ireland also includes a specific target to reduce household waste generation. This will require a positive commitment from individual householders backed up by advice and publicity from the local authorities. It may be obvious that waste is not a problem if it doesn't get produced in the first place, but this is one of the key messages of this block.

SAQ 3

Methane poses two main risks to public health and the environment. Firstly, it is flammable and potentially explosive if it is allowed to accumulate (in the cellars of buildings, for example). Secondly, methane is a powerful greenhouse gas and it is estimated that its contribution to this effect is up to 60 times that of an equal mass of carbon dioxide.

SAQ 4

Adapting the formula for compound interest for this example we have

$$A = P\left(1 + \frac{x}{100}\right)^t$$

where

A is the total amount of waste after a time of t years

P is the amount of waste in the initial year

x is the waste growth rate as %

t is the time period we are considering

For a growth rate of 1% per year

$$A = 30\left(1 + \frac{1}{100}\right)^{20}$$

$$A = 30 \times 1.01^{20}$$

$$A = 30 \times 1.22$$

$$A = 36.6 \text{ million tonnes per year}$$

For a 3% annual growth rate

$$A = 30\left(1 + \frac{3}{100}\right)^{20}$$

$$A = 30 \times 1.03^{20}$$

$$A = 30 \times 1.806$$

$$A = 54.2 \text{ million tonnes per year}$$

SAQ 5

$$14 = 8\left(1 + \frac{x}{100}\right)^{34}$$

$$\frac{14}{8} = \left(1 + \frac{x}{100}\right)^{34}$$

$$1.75 = \left(1 + \frac{x}{100}\right)^{34}$$

$$\log 1.75 = 34 \log\left(1 + \frac{x}{100}\right)$$

$$\frac{\log 1.75}{34} = \log\left(1 + \frac{x}{100}\right)$$

$$\frac{0.243}{34} = \log\left(1 + \frac{x}{100}\right)$$

$$0.007147 = \log\left(1 + \frac{x}{100}\right)$$

$$10^{0.007147} = 1 + \frac{x}{100}$$

$$1.0166 = 1 + \frac{x}{100}$$

$$\frac{x}{100} = 0.0166$$

$$\therefore x = 1.66$$

SAQ 6

For any component we can say

% in overall waste = % in household collected waste $\times 0.75$ + % in CA waste $\times 0.25$

For paper and card

% in overall waste = $23.6 \times 0.75 + 9.29 \times 0.25$

$$= 20.0$$

Doing a similar calculation for all the other fractions we get the following table:

Waste category	Composition (%)
Paper and card	20.0
Plastic film	3.2
Dense plastic	5.3
Textiles	4.6
Wood, carpets and furniture	7.3
Other miscellaneous combustible items	5.1
Construction and demolition waste	5.5
Other miscellaneous non-combustible materials	1.2
Glass	6.1
Kitchen waste	19.4
Garden waste	10.7
Ferrous metal	4.2
Non-ferrous metal	1.0
Waste electrical and electronic equipment	2.8
Potentially hazardous material	0.8
Fines	3.6

SAQ 7

Amount of ash generated $= 46 \times \dfrac{8}{100} = 3.68$ million tonnes

Amount recycled $= 1.84$ million tonnes

Cost saving $= 1.84 \times 10^6 \times 12 = £22\,080\,000$ per year

SAQ 8

Unlike MSW, industrial and commercial wastes tend to:

■   be produced in a relatively concentrated form;

■   have a known composition;

■   be relatively free from impurities.

They can often be recycled with little sorting and processing. In addition, the producers pay directly for their disposal and have a strong incentive to find lower cost disposal routes. Producer responsibility is also placing statutory obligations on producers of certain materials to ensure high recycling rates.

SAQ 9

A short list is shown below, and you have probably selected other types of materials or added different reasons for including the same materials that I selected.

Material	Reason
Acids/alkalis	Cause burns
Batteries	May contain toxic metals and/or acids
Medical items (wipes, swabs, dressings, syringes, etc.)	Danger of infection
Pharmaceuticals/drugs	Possibly harmful if ingested
Flammable liquids	Risk of fire/explosion
Substances containing heavy metals (lead, cadmium, mercury, etc.)	Range of toxic effects if ingested
Old pesticides and herbicides	Toxic

You may have concentrated on health or environmental effects, thought about biological risks (infection, etc.) or physical risks (cuts, etc.), or considered the amount or concentration of harmful material that must be present.

Whatever criteria you selected you probably concluded that there are many ways to define hazardous wastes.

SAQ 10

The key provisions are:

■ hazardous wastes will only be allowed in landfill sites designated as hazardous waste sites and not co-disposed of with other wastes;

■ some hazardous wastes (explosive, flammable, corrosive) will not be allowed in any landfilled sites.

The effect of this will be a reduction in the amount of hazardous waste sent to landfill and an increase in the costs of landfilling the wastes that continue to be disposed of in this way.

SAQ 11

■ the use of rural (possibly undeveloped) land for quarrying;

■ visual impacts, dust and noise due to quarrying;

■ reduction in value of land and properties in the neighbourhood of the quarry;

■ depletion of possibly finite resources;

■ transport of quarried materials from rural to urban areas for use;

■ transport of the wastes to landfill (often from urban to rural areas);

■ operation of the landfill site (noise, visual, dusts, etc.).

SAQ 12

- hospitals
- GP surgeries/clinics
- dental surgeries
- residential care homes
- podiatrists
- acupuncture clinics
- undertakers
- pharmacies
- research establishments (pharmaceuticals, universities, military)
- veterinary surgeries
- the home (syringes and medicines, etc. used by diabetics and other conditions treated by the patient).

SAQ 13

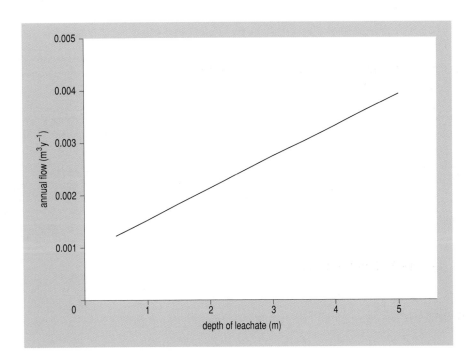

SAQ 14

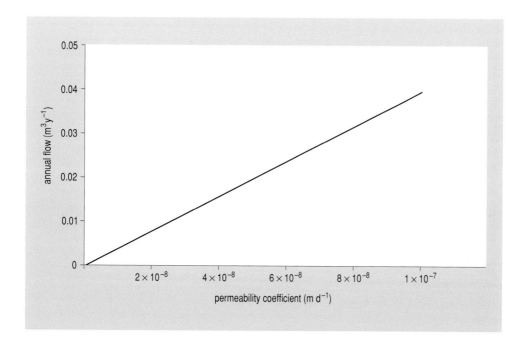

SAQ 15

We begin all calculations of this nature by stating our starting basis. In this case, we will consider 1 tonne of waste. This will contain

240 kg or $\dfrac{240}{12} = 20$ kmol of carbon

30 kg or $\dfrac{30}{1} = 30$ kmol of hydrogen (15 kmol of H_2)

1 kg or $\dfrac{1}{32} = 0.03$ kmol of sulphur

280 or $\dfrac{280}{16} = 17.5$ kmol of oxygen (8.75 kmol of O_2)

The combustion equations involved are

$C + O_2 \longrightarrow CO_2$

$2H_2 + O_2 \longrightarrow 2H_2O$

$S + O_2 \longrightarrow SO_2$

So

1 kmol of C reacts with 1 kmol of O_2 and 20 kmol reacts with 20 kmol of O_2;

2 kmol of H_2 reacts with 1 kmol of O_2 and 15 kmol reacts with 7.5 kmol of O_2;

1 kmol of S reacts with 1 kmol of O_2 and 0.03 kmol reacts with 0.03 kmol of O_2.

So the total amount of O_2 required is $20 + 7.5 + 0.03 = 27.53$ kmol

But the waste itself contains 8.75 kmol of O_2 so the net amount required is $27.53 - 8.75 = 18.78$ kmol of O_2.

So the volume of oxygen required is $18.78 \times 22.4 = 421$ m^3 (under standard conditions).

Air contains 21% by volume oxygen so the theoretical volume of air required is

$$421 \times \frac{100}{21} = 2005 \text{ m}^3 \text{ per tonne of waste}$$

If the required air supply is 190% of the theoretical requirement we can say that

$$\text{Air required} = 2005 \times \frac{190}{100} = 3810 \text{ m}^3$$

Volume of nitrogen:

$$3810 \times \frac{79}{100} = 3010 \text{ m}^3 \text{ (from the combustion air)}$$

Volume of oxygen:

$$3810 \times \frac{21}{100} - 421 = 379 \text{ m}^3 \text{ (amount in the air supplied less the amount}$$

consumed in the reactions)

Volume of carbon dioxide:

20 kmol is formed by the combustion of 20 kmol of carbon, which has a volume of $20 \times 22.4 = 448$ m^3 (under standard conditions)

Volume of water:

15 kmol is formed by the combustion of 15 kmol of hydrogen, and the waste feed contains 270 kg or $\frac{270}{18} = 15$ kmol of water. So the total amount of water is $15 + 15 = 30$ kmol or $30 \times 22.4 = 672$ m^3 (under standard conditions).

So the flue gas contains:

Component	Volume (m^3 per tonne of waste burned)	Percentage
Nitrogen	3010	67
Oxygen	379	8
Carbon dioxide	448	10
Water	672	15
Total	4509	

SAQ 16

The first step is to convert the 800 ppm from volume to mass units. Volume of HCl present is

$$6000 \times \frac{800}{1\,000\,000} = 4.8 \text{ m}^3$$

We know that 22.4 m^3 of gas is occupied by 1 kmol, so the mass of HCl present is given by

$$\frac{4.8}{22.4} = 0.21 \text{ kmol}$$

The relative molecular mass of HCl is $1 + 35.5 = 36.5$.

So 0.21 kmol has a mass of $0.21 \times 36.5 = 7.67$ kg.

So the concentration of HCl in mass units is $\frac{7.67}{6000} = 0.0013$ kg m^{-3} or 1300 mg m^{-3}.

The required removal efficiency is given by $\frac{1300 - 10}{1300} \times 100 = 99.2\%$

The scrubbing reaction given in Section 9.5.1 is

$$Ca(OH)_2 + 2HCl \longrightarrow CaCl_2 + 2H_2O$$

From each 6000 m^3 of flue gas we need to remove $6000 \times (1300 - 10) = 7\,740\,000$ mg or 7.74 kg of HCl.

The scrubbing reaction tells us that 1 mole of lime removes 2 moles of HCl (i.e. $40 + 2\{16 + 1\} = 74$ g of lime, removes $2\{1 + 35.5\} = 73$ g of HCl).

Therefore to remove 7.74 kg of HCl, we need (74 g lime/73 g HCl) $\times$ 7.74 kg HCl = 7.846 kg lime. Say, 7.85 kg lime.

So we need 7.85 kg of lime per tonne of waste burned (of course this is the theoretical amount, and the actual amount required would be much greater).

SAQ 17

The equation tells us that four moles of ammonia are required to reduce two moles of NO$_2$. The atomic mass of NO$_2$ is $14 + (2 \times 16) = 46$ and that of ammonia is $14 + (3 \times 1) = 17$.

So $4 \times 17 = 68$ g of ammonia reduces $2 \times 46 = 92$ g of NO$_2$

or 1 g of NO$_2$ is reduced by $\frac{68}{92} = 0.739$ g of ammonia.

For each tonne of waste burned we need to reduce

$$6000 \times \left(\frac{400 - 200}{1000} \right) = 1200 \text{ g of NO}_2$$

which requires $1200 \times 0.739 = 887$ g of ammonia.

SAQ 18

Referring to the table produced in SAQ 6, the following materials will be suitable for AD:

- paper and card (20% of the total);

- natural textiles (say 50% of the textiles fraction) (2.3% of the total);

- kitchen and garden waste (30.1% of the total).

So we can say that about 52% of household waste can be treated by AD. In fact the figure may be even higher because a proportion of the fines fraction will be degradable and some of the miscellaneous combustible fraction may also degrade if the particle size is small enough.

SAQ 19

Under the new definition the total amount of municipal waste is $35 + 41 = 76$ Mt
The amount recycled is given by

$$35 \times \frac{25}{100} + 41 \times \frac{42}{100} = 25.97 \text{ Mt}$$

So our revised recycling rate is now $\frac{25.9}{76} \times 100 = 34\%$.

So, with the aid of a simple calculation it is possible to increase the recycling rate by 9 percentage points without having to bother to collect a single additional tonne of waste!

SAQ 20

The following table can be constructed using the percentage composition of household waste calculated in SAQ 6.

Component	Composition of household waste (%)	% recyclable	Maximum theoretical recycling rate (%)
Paper and card	20	90	18.0
Dense plastic	5.3	30	1.6
Glass	6.1	95	5.8
Ferrous metal	4.2	70	2.9
Non-ferrous metal	1.0	30	0.3
Kitchen/garden waste	30.1	80	24.1
Remainder	33.3	0	0
Total			52.7

So the maximum recycling rate is about 53% and the average household can recycle a maximum of $1150 \times \frac{53}{100} = 609.5$, say 610 kg per year.

SAQ 21

Firstly, we need to calculate the proportion of each recyclable material that householders actually put out for recycling (this allows for the fact that not everyone will want to rinse out their food cans, etc.).

Material	Proportion of material that is theoretically recyclable (%)	Proportion of material that householders put out for recycling (%)	Proportion of material actually recycled (%)
Paper and card	90	90	81
Dense plastic	30	50	15
Glass	95	80	76
Ferrous metal	70	50	35
Non-ferrous metal	30	70	21
Compostable waste	80	70	56

From this and the data from SAQ 6 we can calculate the proportion of each type of household waste that is actually recycled.

Component	Proportion of waste actually recycled (%)	Composition of household waste (%) (from SAQ 6)	Proportion of waste that is recycled as percentage of total household waste (%)
Paper and card	81	20.0	16.2
Dense plastics	15	5.3	0.8
Glass	76	6.1	4.6
Ferrous metal	35	4.2	1.5
Non-ferrous metal	21	1.0	0.2
Kitchen/garden waste	56	30.1	16.9
Remainder	0	33.3	0
Total		100	40.2

Adding the figures in the final column together tells us that a total of about 40% of household waste would be recycled in such a UK-wide scheme. But, we also need to take account of the 25% of households that do not participate. This reduces our recycling rate to

$$40.2 \times \frac{75}{100} = 30.2\%$$

Then again, if we are concerned with the amount of material leaving the MRFs and compost production plants we need to take account of the material rejected in these processes (which I have assumed is about 5%). So our recycling rate is now

$$30.2 \times \frac{95}{100} = 28.7\%$$

SAQ 22

Impact	Mitigation method
Visual impact	Sympathetic design of external structure Use of earth bunds and planting to act as screens
Dust	Tipping area enclosed and doors to be closed during tipping
Odours	Building maintained at negative pressure All air discharges through de-dusters Use of odour masking agents
Noise	Tipping carried out when doors closed Noisy operations enclosed in acoustically-screened cabins Operations restricted to 'office hours'
Traffic	Vehicles use designated routes avoiding residential areas Deliveries and collections restricted to 'office hours'

SAQ 23

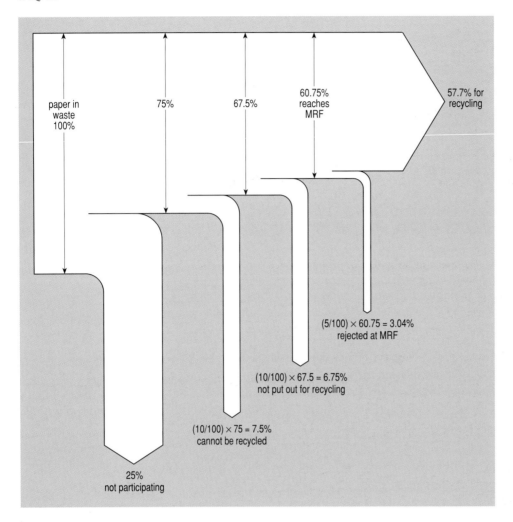

SAQ 24

The steep gradient tells us that in the early stages the process is very rapid with the rate of the reactions slowing down with time. From the operator's point of view this means that pile heating and oxygen consumption will be at a maximum in the early stages so the compost will require frequent turning in the first few weeks.

SAQ 25

My list included:

- using scrap paper for shopping lists and notes;
- using supermarket carrier bags as bin liners;
- registering with the direct mail preference service to reduce 'junk mail';
- buying loose rather than pre-packed fruit and vegetables;
- passing outgrown children's clothes to a friend;
- buying detergents, etc. in refillable containers;
- only buying a newspaper when I really have time to read it (rather than daily).

The biggest change I could make would be to start composting my garden waste at home.

SAQ 26

(a) Paper costs:

$$840 \times 11 = £9240 \text{ per year}$$

disposal costs:

$$11 \times \frac{70}{100} \times 45 = £346.50, \text{ say } £347 \text{ per year}$$

total costs: £9587 per year

(b) The company's paper consumption falls to 90% of its previous level, so it now costs

$$£9240 \times 0.9 = £8316 \text{ per year}$$

There is also a saving in the disposal costs, which is equal to

$$£347 \times 0.9 = £312.30, \text{ say } £312 \text{ per year}$$

So the total annual cost of the paper is $£8316 + £312 = £8628$.

This is a saving of £959 per year compared with scenario (a).

(c) The cost of buying the paper remains at £8316 per year, but instead of a disposal cost of £312 there is now an income of

$$0.9 \times 11 \times \frac{70}{100} \times 10 = £69.30, \text{ say } £69 \text{ per year}$$

So the total costs are now

$$£8316 - £69 = £8247$$

This represents a saving of

$$\frac{9587 - 8247}{9587} \times 100 = 13.98, \text{ say } 14\%$$

SAQ 27

These costs assume that the compostable waste is collected in a separate collection round from the other waste. This extra collection will double the total cost of waste collection. However, this additional round will only collect a maximum of 20–25% of the weight of material collected on the main round, but will take just as long to complete and use the same amount of fuel. Therefore the cost per tonne can be very high.

The wide range of values is due to two factors. Firstly, low participation makes the cost per tonne collected even higher and secondly, the cost of servicing a given number of households is generally lower in densely populated urban areas than in rural areas where the distances travelled and time taken are longer.

SAQ 28

To reduce these costs we need to consider both the costs per tonne of material collected and the total collection costs.

The first can be reduced by maximizing the amount of material collected. This can be achieved by a combination of publicity campaigns, making participation easy (e.g. by ensuring that collections take place at the same time on the same day each week) and making the collection service as reliable as possible.

It may be possible to reduce the total cost by combining the collections of recyclable materials and the residual waste in an adapted vehicle with two or more compartments.

Other ways of increasing participation and reducing total costs might be to reduce the size of the residual waste container or reduce its collection frequency from weekly to fortnightly. Either measure would reduce the amount of material that householders could dispose of in their residual waste container, so forcing them to increase their use of the compost and recyclables collections.

SAQ 29

External costs from incineration could include:

Costs	Benefits
■ Impacts of manufacturing steel, concrete, etc. used in constructing the facility	■ Savings of fossil fuel resources
■ Impacts of landfilling residues (including some special waste)	■ Saving of impacts associated with metals (and possibly aggregate) extraction and processing
■ Acidification (due to HCl, SO_2 and NO_x emissions)	■ Reduction in SO_2 emissions through reduced coal consumption
■ Heavy metal and dioxin emissions	■ Reduction in impact of MSW landfill
■ Site impacts (noise, visual, odours, etc.)	
■ Water pollution from boiler water discharges, plant cleaning, etc.	

Of course many of these costs would apply (to differing extents) to all waste management processes.

SAQ 30

(a)

Waste category	A	B	C
	Proportion in original waste (%)	Amount removed (A × % recovery)	Amount remaining (A − B)
Paper and card	20.0	8.0	12.0
Plastic film	3.2	0	3.2
Dense plastic	5.3	1.33	3.97
Textiles	4.6	0	4.6
Wood, carpets and furniture	7.3	0	7.3
Other miscellaneous combustible items	5.1	0	5.1
Construction and demolition waste	5.5	0	5.5
Other miscellaneous non-combustible materials	1.2	0	1.2
Glass	6.1	4.88	1.22
Kitchen waste	19.4	0	19.4
Garden waste	10.7	0	10.7
Ferrous metal	4.2	2.1	2.1
Non-ferrous metal	1.0	0.5	0.5
Waste electrical and electronic equipment	2.8	0	2.8
Potentially hazardous material	0.8	0	0.8
Fines	3.6	0	3.6
Total			83.99

So 84% of the waste is available for incineration (although in practice the construction and demolition waste, electrical and electronic equipment, potentially hazardous material and a proportion of the other miscellaneous categories would not be suitable for incineration.

(b) Repeating the calculation we find that 78% of the original mass is available for incineration.

(c) Repeating it again we find that 61% is still available for incineration.

SAQ 31

(a) Starting with 100 kg of waste:

Waste category	A	B	C	D
	Mass in raw waste (kg)	Mass for incineration (kg)	Calorific value (MJ kg^{-1})	Heat content of component (MJ) (B × C)
Paper and card	20.0	20.0	12.58	251.6
Plastic film	3.2	3.2	23.6	75.5
Dense plastics	5.3	5.3	26.7	141.5
Textiles	4.6	4.6	15.9	73.1
Wood, carpets and furniture	7.3	7.3	11.6	84.7
Other miscellaneous combustible items	5.1	5.1	11.6	59.2
Construction and demolition waste	5.5	0	0	0.0
Other miscellaneous non-combustible materials	1.2	1.2	2.8	3.4
Glass	6.1	6.1	0	0.0
Kitchen waste	19.4	19.4	5.5	106.7
Garden waste	10.7	10.7	5.5	58.9
Ferrous metal	4.2	4.2	0	0.0
Non-ferrous metal	1.0	1.0	0	0.0
Waste electrical and electronic equipment	2.8	0	0	0.0
Potentially hazardous material	0.8	0	0	0.0
Fines	3.6	3.6	4.8	17.3
Total		91.7		871.9

So the calorific value is given by

$$\frac{871.9}{91.7} = 9.51 \text{ MJ kg}^{-1}$$

(b)

Waste category	A Mass in raw waste (kg)	B Mass for incineration (kg)	C Calorific value (MJ kg^{-1})	D Heat content of component (MJ) (B × C)
Paper and card	20.0	12.0	12.58	151.0
Plastic film	3.2	3.2	23.6	75.5
Dense plastic	5.3	4.0	26.7	106.8
Textiles	4.6	4.6	15.9	73.1
Wood, carpets and furniture	7.3	7.3	11.6	84.7
Other miscellaneous combustible items	5.1	5.1	11.6	59.2
Construction and demolition waste	5.5	0	0	0.0
Other miscellaneous non-combustible materials	1.2	1.2	2.8	3.4
Glass	6.1	1.2	0	0.0
Kitchen waste	19.4	3.9	5.5	21.5
Garden waste	10.7	2.1	5.5	11.6
Ferrous metal	4.2	2.1	0	0.0
Non-ferrous metal	1.0	0.5	0	0.0
Waste electrical and electronic equipment	2.8	0	0	0.0
Potentially hazardous material	0.8	0	0	0.0
Fines	3.6	3.6	4.8	17.3
Total		50.8		604.1

So the calorific value is given by

$$\frac{604.1}{50.8} = 11.89 \text{ MJ kg}^{-1}$$

SAQ 32

■ adsorption – reversible;

■ absorption – reversible;

■ ion exchange – reversible;

■ chemical reaction – irreversible in some cases (e.g. neutralization); some reactions (e.g. precipitation) may be reversible if conditions such as pH change;

■ biodegradation – irreversible;

■ dilution – irreversible, but persistent materials may be bioaccumulated subsequently;

■ filtration – irreversible, although filtered material may be changed chemically and then become mobile again.

SAQ 33

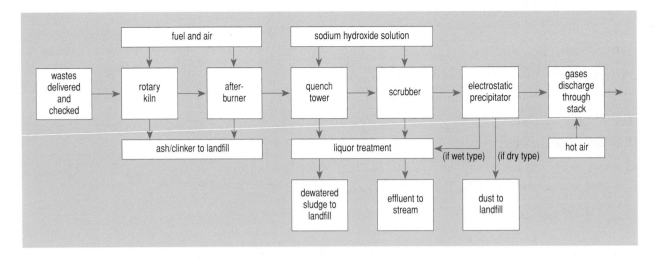

SAQ 34

The chlorine in the molecule will be emitted as hydrogen chloride while the fluorine will appear as hydrogen fluoride. Both are toxic and corrosive and will need to be scrubbed. Excessive levels of fluorides in the scrubber and quench waters could cause water pollution if not treated.

If other wastes are being burned at the same time there is the possibility of dioxin formation; hence combustion conditions must be carefully controlled.

Additionally, these compounds generate reactive species called free radicals which inhibit combustion. This may cause problems in maintaining adequate combustion conditions and limits the rate at which CFCs can be burned (you are not expected to know this but it may be of interest).

SAQ 35

Total mass of PCBs burned per day $= 25 \times 2/100 \times 24$ kg.

Daily emissions of PCBs are therefore

$$\frac{(100.0000 - 99.9999)}{100} \times (25 \times \frac{2}{100} \times 24) \text{ kg}$$

$$= 0.000012 \text{ kg}$$

SAQ 36

1   It is easier to ensure an adequate excess of oxygen if the pure gas is used.

2   When air is used, some of the heat produced during combustion is wasted in heating up nitrogen, which makes up about four-fifths of the air. Using pure oxygen can thus increase the fuel efficiency of the plant and is often economical as a result, despite the extra cost of the oxygen.

3   With less air present there is less nitrogen, and the production of nitrogen oxides is reduced, although they may still be formed if the wastes contain nitrogen.

SAQ 37

Plasma torches operate at 5000–10 000 °C, whereas high-temperature incinerators operate at up to 1300 °C.

Plasma torches can only handle pumpable wastes with minimal solids, whereas incinerators can handle solids, slurries and drummed wastes as well.

Incinerators operate under oxidizing conditions, whereas plasma torches operate under reducing conditions. This has implications for dioxin production.

SAQ 38

A High temperature incineration.

B Plasma torches.

C Infra-red heating.

D Oxidation with alkali and polyethylene glycol.

E Dechlorination with alkali metal, e.g. sodium.

F Biological treatment.

G Electrochemical incineration.

A, B, D, E, and G are suitable for liquids, and C may be suitable for capacitors, etc., containing liquid PCBs; A, C, D and F may be suitable for contaminated soil.

SAQ 39

(a) Acetic acid is a naturally occurring compound. It may be treated biologically although it may need to be diluted since a very low pH may inhibit microbial action.

(b) Tetraethyl lead is not amenable to biological treatment. Even if the ethyl groups could be removed biologically, the lead would remain permanently.

(c) DDT is difficult to degrade biologically as it is an organochlorine compound. Some promising organisms are being developed and these may be usable in the future.

(d) Phenol is treatable biologically at low concentrations. High concentrations are biocidal – it is used as an antiseptic and disinfectant.

(e) CFCs (chlorofluorocarbons) are not treatable biologically.

SAQ 40

The more familiar form of hydrogen has a form of ^1_1H and has one proton with a mass number of 1. Deuterium, ^2_1H, has one proton and one neutron, and a mass number of 2.

Given that isotopes of the same element all contain the same number of protons, the atomic number of all hydrogen isotopes will be 1.

SAQ 41

The Sun has a power output of 4×10^{26} W and Sizewell B has a power output of 1.2×10^9 W.

The number of power stations needed would therefore be $4 \times 10^{26} / 1.2 \times 10^9 = 3.3 \times 10^{17}$.

SAQ 42

Isotope	Number of neutrons	Ratio of neutrons/protons	Stability
$^{14}_6C$	$14 - 6 = 8$	$8/6 = 1.3$	unstable
$^{14}_7N$	$14 - 7 = 7$	$7/7 = 1$	stable
$^{22}_{10}Ne$	$22 - 10 = 12$	$12/10 = 1.2$	unstable
$^{22}_{11}Na$	$22 - 11 = 11$	$11/11 = 1$	stable
$^{184}_{82}Pb$	$184 - 82 = 102$	$102/82 = 1.24$	unstable
$^{180}_{80}Hg$	$180 - 80 = 100$	$100/80 = 1.25$	unstable

SAQ 43

(a) You would expect the α-particles, which are positively charged, to be attracted to the negatively charged plate and repelled by the positively charged plate.

Conversely, the β-particles, which are negatively charged, will be attracted to the positive plate and repelled by the negative plate.

The γ-rays, which are uncharged, will be unaffected by the plates. Thus the α-particles are expected to move towards the negative plate and the β-particles deflected towards the positive plate.

(b) Consider the negatively charged plate. This attracts α-particles. However, each time an α-particle strikes the plate, it will neutralize two of the negative charges on the plate; so in time the total negative charge will be neutralized. A similar effect will occur on the positively charged plate due to capture of β-particles; in this case, because β-particles have a single charge, the neutralizing effect will be much slower.

SAQ 44

(a) The three reactions are

$$^{233}_{92}U \longrightarrow {}^{229}_{90}Th + \alpha$$

$$^{229}_{90}Th \longrightarrow {}^{225}_{88}Ra + \alpha$$

$$^{225}_{88}Ra \longrightarrow {}^{225}_{89}Ac + \beta$$

(b)

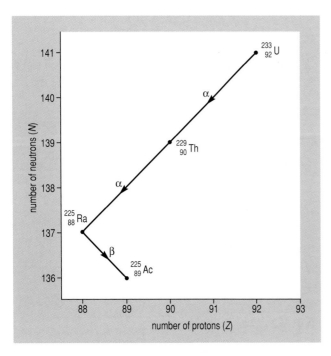

SAQ 45

(a) The reaction can be written as

$$^{198}_{79}Au \longrightarrow {}^{198}_{80}Hg + \beta + \gamma$$

(b) Equation 2 can be written as

$$I = I_0 e^{-\left(\frac{\ln 2}{t_{\frac{1}{2}}}\right)t}$$

Where $I_0 = 10^6$ units, $t_{\frac{1}{2}} = 2.7$ days, $t = 7$ days

So

$$I = 10^6 e^{-\left(\frac{\ln 2}{2.7}\right)\times 7}$$

$$= 1.66 \times 10^5 \text{ units}$$

Therefore, after seven days the activity of the source is 1.66×10^5 units and there are 1.66×10^5 disintegrations per second. Since each disintegration emits two 'particles', the material emits $2 \times 1.66 \times 10^5 = 3.32 \times 10^5$ particles per second.

SAQ 46

You may have considered a number of different precautions. Those recommended by the International Commission of Radiological Protection (ICRP) depend on the magnitude of the accident and include:

■ sheltering to reduce external radiation, inhalation as the cloud passes and skin irradiation (particularly from the β-emitters Kr and Xe);

■ distribution of stable iodine tablets to help prevent the concentration of radioactive iodine (iodine 131) in the thyroid gland;

■ evacuation;

■ restrictions on food and water (particularly important to reduce uptake of caesium through milk and meat because of the long half life of Cs 137);

■ long-term relocation of the population.

SAQ 47

(a) Energy of β-particle $= 0.5$ MeV $= 0.5 \times 10^6$ eV

Track length $= 2$ mm $= 2 \times 10^3$ μm

So LET $=$ energy deposited/track length

$$= \frac{0.5 \times 10^6}{2 \times 10^3} \text{ eV μm}^{-1}$$

$$= 250 \text{ eV μm}^{-1} = 0.25 \text{ keV μm}^{-1}$$

(b) Track length $= 2$ mm $= 2 \times 10^3$ μm

LET $= 10$ keV μm$^{-1} = 10^4$ eV μm^{-1}

LET $=$ energy deposited (E)/track length

$$10^4 = \frac{E}{2 \times 10^3}$$

$$E = 2 \times 10^7 \text{eV}$$

$$= 20 \text{ MeV}$$

SAQ 48

(a) There is a lack of data about health effects from high LET radiation. Most of the data are from the survivors of the atomic bombings which were acute doses of low LET rather than high LET radiation. Only some data from uranium miners exists for high LET radiation but that may not be representative of critical groups such as women and children.

(b) If we use a linear model when the linear-quadratic one is correct we will be overestimating the risk; conversely, if we use a linear-quadratic model when we should be using a linear one we will underestimate the risk.

SAQ 49

(a)

Dose range (Sv)	Average dose (Sv)	Number of subjects	Number of expected background cancer deaths	Number of observed cancer deaths	Number of excess cancers
0–0.009	0.004	36 132	2725.9	2562	−163.9
0.01–0.05	0.02	19 518	1408.1	1394	−14.1
0.06–0.09	0.07	4113	336.5	341	4.5
0.10–0.19	0.13	5209	412.6	410	−2.6
0.20–0.49	0.31	6218	499.9	529	29.1
0.50–0.99	0.69	2829	214.0	273	59.0
1.0–1.99	1.36	1380	101.8	158	56.2
2.0–2.99	2.34	361	20.4	37	16.6
3.0–3.99	3.51	147	9.3	20	10.7
4.0+	4.41	84	5.5	10	4.5

(b) The numbers do not demonstrate a very close relationship at all doses. At very low doses and at 0.13 Sv the number of cancers was less than the expected background, but as the dose increases to about 0.31 Sv and 0.69 Sv there is an upward trend, with increasing excess cancers with increasing dose. At very high doses the figures are reducing and less certain, particularly bearing in mind the lower number of subjects.

SAQ 50

One of the most serious threats to the global environment, from burning fossil fuels, comes from greenhouse gases such as carbon dioxide. Since nuclear power produces very little carbon dioxide it could be seen as a viable alternative to fossil fuels. Average doses to the global population from current nuclear power are very small compared with those from natural radiation.

SAQ 51

(a) $^{131}_{53}I$ decays by β-emission, so that the mass number remains unchanged at 131. However, the loss of a single negative charge means that the atomic number increases by one to 54. This is xenon, Xe. So the decay product is $^{131}_{54}Xe$.

(b) On Day 2, the activity of the concentrated solution will have decreased. The activity can be calculated using Equation 2

$$N = N_0 e^{-\left(\frac{\ln 2}{t_{\frac{1}{2}}}\right)t}$$

and replacing the number of atoms, N, by the intensity, I

$$I = I_0 e^{-\left(\frac{\ln 2}{t_{\frac{1}{2}}}\right)t}$$

where $I_0 = 1$ MBq (10^6 Bq), $t = 1$ day, and $t_{\frac{1}{2}} = 8$ days.

So

$$I = 10^6 e^{-\left(\frac{\ln 2}{8}\right)\times 1}$$

$$= 0.917 \times 10^6 \text{ Bq}$$

(c) The activity of 30 ml of the solution
$$= (30/1000) \times 0.917 \times 10^6 \text{ Bq} = 27.51 \times 10^3 \text{ Bq}.$$

If volume of water added is x litres, then $(x + 0.03)$ litres has an activity of 27.51×10^3 Bq.

The final solution has an activity of 10 000 Bq per litre.

Therefore

$$\frac{27.51 \times 10^3}{(x + 0.03)} \text{ Bq l}^{-1} = 10000 \text{ Bq l}^{-1}$$

$$(x + 0.03)1 = \frac{27.51 \times 10^3}{10000} \frac{\text{Bq}}{\text{Bq l}^{-1}}$$

$$x = 2.751 - 0.03 = 2.721 \text{ litres}$$

$$x = 2721 \text{ ml}$$

(d) The total starting activity is 27.51×10^3 Bq; 30% of this in ingested by the patient.

So initial activity of patient $= 0.3 \times 27.51 \times 10^3$ Bq $= 8.253 \times 10^3$ Bq

The residual solution is 200 ml

So activity of residual solution $= 200/2751 \times 27.51 \times 10^3$ Bq $= 2 \times 10^3$ Bq

Activity accounted for $= (8.253 + 2) \times 10^3$ Bq $= 10.253 \times 10^3$ Bq

(i) So radioactivity unaccounted for $= (27.51 - 10.253) \times 10^3$ Bq $= 17.257 \times 10^3$ Bq

(ii) Radioactivity of residual solution $= 2 \times 10^3$ Bq.

SAQ 52

Beyond nuclear accidents the primary concern with any expansion of nuclear power is the management of radioactive waste. Nuclear power stations generate both LILW and HLW wastes. LILW still needs containment and isolation for up to 300 years, with associated administrative and institutional control. HLW, such as spent fuel from nuclear reactors, needs safe isolation beyond existing generations and there are as yet no proven methods for its disposal.

SAQ 53

Contaminant	Waste classification
PTEs (cadmium, lead, arsenic, mercury)	Hazardous waste (toxic and some PTEs are also carcinogenic)
Other metals	Could be hazardous waste if concentrations are high enough (toxic, harmful)
Combustible substances	Low flash-point oils would be hazardous waste (flammable) Coal and coke would not normally be hazardous waste, but fine dusts may be classed as hazardous (highly flammable)
Flammable gases	Hazardous waste (highly flammable)
Aggressive substances	Hazardous waste (irritant, corrosive or toxic – depending on substances present)
Oily and tarry substances	Hazardous waste (could well be flammable, carcinogenic, mutagenic, or toxic)
Asbestos	Hazardous waste (carcinogenic)

SAQ 54

Treatment	Sustainability
Excavation and landfill	Landfill may isolate the contamination in the short term, but is not sustainable. It leaves future generations with the responsibility for maintaining the landfill pollution control mechanisms and for finally processing the contaminated material.
Containment/encapsulation	Again, these can be seen as short-term solutions that isolate the contaminants from the environment. However, they are not sustainable because the isolation method will fail eventually, leaving the contamination for future generations to deal with.
Stabilization/solidification	These methods are advanced versions of containment/encapsulation techniques. Material subjected to these methods of treatment (radioactive waste for example) and stored in underground salt deposits will be isolated from the environment for thousands of years. Some would define this as sustainable, while others would say the opposite.
Thermal treatment	These processes can destroy organic contaminants, but may be regarded as unsustainable if the combustion process produced by-products that require permanent storage.
Solvent extraction	Such processes remove the contamination in an effective manner, but leave a residue for incineration (see above).
Chemical treatment	Some classes of inorganic compounds can be destroyed, but like thermal treatment the creation of by-products would make this unsustainable.
Bioremediation	Micro-organisms degrade organic pollutants into harmless compounds. As such, the processes can be considered to be sustainable, but there are questions over the effectiveness and speed of decontamination.
Physical treatment	Venting or vacuum extraction has the potential to return the soil to its pre-contaminated state and, if the exhaust gas is burned in a high temperature combustor, it will produce minimal residues for final disposal. Soil washing concentrates the contaminants in 10-30% of the original soil mass, so does leave some residue for long-term disposal to landfill. However, you may take the view that the reduction in the volume of contaminated material is a move towards sustainability.
Dilution	Dilution reduces contamination levels to what are considered to be acceptable concentrations by today's standards. On these grounds you may consider the technique to be sustainable. However, changes in standards or proposed future uses of the land may mean that further remediation is required in the future. You may regard this practice of 'putting off taking action' to be unsustainable.

REFERENCES

Atkinson, W. and New, R. (1993) 'Kerbside collection of recyclables from household waste in the UK – a position study', Warren Spring Laboratory.

Best Foot Forward (2001) 'Island state: an ecological footprint analysis of the Isle of Wight', Biffaward programme on sustainable resource use, Best Foot Forward.

Border, D. (2003) 'A review of composting of controlled wastes', Environment Agency Technical Report, in preparation.

Boulos, S., Pocock, R. and Gilbert, E. (2006), 'The state of composting and biological waste treatment in the UK', The Composting Association, Wellingborough.

Bridgwater, A. (1986) 'Refuse composition projects and recycling technology', *Resources and Conservation*, vol. 12, pp.159–74.

British Standards Institution (2005), 'Specification for composted materials', PAS 100:2005, London.

Brown, K. A., Smith, A., Burnley, S. J., Campbell, D. J. V., King, K. and Milton, M. J. T. (1999) 'Methane emissions from UK landfills', AEA Report 5217.

Burnley, S. J. and Aplin, P. (1999) 'Controlling oxides of nitrogen emissions from a municipal-waste incinerator by flue gas recirculation', *Journal of the Institute of Energy*, pp.165–9.

Burnley, S. J., Coleman, T. and Gronow, J. R. (1999) 'The impact of the landfill directive on strategic waste management in the UK', in *Landfill Processes and Waste Pre-treatment*, vol. IV, International Conference on Landfill, Sardinia.

Burnley, S. J., Ellis, J. C., Flowerdew, R., Poll, A. J. and Prosser, H. (2007), 'Assessing the composition of municipal solid waste in Wales', *Resources, Conservation and Recycling*, **49** (3) 264–283.

Burnley, S. J. and Parfitt, J. P. (2000) 'Public attitudes to waste and waste management', Onyx Environmental Trust.

Chiras, D. (1998) *Environmental Science: A Systems Approach to Sustainable Development*, Wadsworth Publishing Company.

Composting Association (2000) 'The Composting Association's standards for compost', Composting Association.

Croft, B. and Campbell, W. B. (1990) 'Characterisation of 100 UK landfill sites', Proceedings of Harwell Waste Management Symposium 1990.

Defra (2000) 'Waste strategy 2000', Cmnd 4693-1, Department for Environment, Food and Rural Affairs, The Stationery Office.

Defra (2001) Municipal Waste Management Survey 1999/2000, Department for Environment, Food and Rural Affairs, July 2001, The Stationery Office. Available from http://www.defra.gov.uk/environment/statistics/wastats/archive/index.htm [accessed 31 October 2002].

Defra (2002) 'Dioxin and dioxin-like PCBs in the UK environment', Department for Environment, Food and Rural Affairs, October 2002, The Stationery Office.

Defra (2006), 'Estimated total annual waste arisings by sector', http://www.defra.gov.uk/environment/statistics/waste/kf/wrkf02.htm [accessed 17 January 2007].

Defra (2007), 'Waste Strategy for England 2007', Department for Environment, Food and Rural Affairs, May 2007, The Stationery Office. Available from http://www.defra.gov.uk/environment/waste/strategy/ [accessed 26 September 2007].

DoE (undated) 'Environment in trust', *Radioactive Waste Management – A Safe Solution*, Department of the Environment.

DoE (1997) 'Landfill design, construction and operational practice', Waste Management Paper 26B, Department of the Environment, The Stationery Office.

ENDS (2000) 'Britain's contaminated land liability put at £15 billion', Environmental Data Services (ENDS) Report 305, June 2000.

Environment Agency (1994a), 'National Household Waste Analysis Project Phase 2: Report on composition and weight data Volume 1', CWM 082/94, Environment Agency.

Environment Agency (1994b), 'National Household Waste Analysis Project Phase 2: Report on further composition and weight data', CWM 086/94, Environment Agency.

Environment Agency (1999) 'Survey of remedial techniques for land contamination in England and Wales', Research Report P4-01, Environment Agency.

Environment Agency (2000) 'An assessment of the quality of waste derived composts produced by a range of processes', Technical Report P1-229, Environment Agency.

Environment Agency (2002) [online]. Available from http://www.environment-agency.gov.uk/subjects/waste [accessed 24 October 2002].

Environment Agency (2006), 'Commercial and industrial waste survey 2002/03', http://www.environment-agency.gov.uk/subjects/waste/1031954/315439/923299/1071046/?version=1&lang=_e [accessed 18 January 2007].

Environment Agency (2006), 'Model procedures for the management of contaminated land', Contaminated Land Report 11, The Environment Agency, Bristol.

Environment and Heritage Service (2006), 'Municipal waste management Northern Ireland 2005/06 summary report', Environment and Heritage Service, Belfast.

Council of the European Communities (1975) Directive on waste, 75/442/EEC, *Official Journal of the European Communities* L194, pp.39–41, as amended.

Council of the European Union (1999) Directive on the landfilling of waste, 1999/31/EC, *Official Journal of the European Communities* L182, pp.1–19.

Gladding, T. (undated) 'An assessment of the risks to human health of materials recovery facilities: a framework for decision makers', Environment Agency Report. To be published.

IAEA (2000) 'The safety of radioactive waste management: achieving internationally acceptable solutions', *IAEA Bulletin*, vol. 42, no. 3, International Atomic Energy Authority.

McDougall, F. R. and White, P. R. (2001) *Integrated Solid Waste Management: A Life Cycle Inventory*, Blackwell Science.

NAW (2001) 'Managing waste sustainably', National Assembly for Wales, July 2001. Available from http://www.wales.gov.uk/subienvironment/content/consultations/waste/index.htm [accessed 31 October 2002].

NAW (2006), 'Municipal waste management report for Wales 2004–05', National Assembly for Wales, Cardiff.

NIEHS (2000) 'Waste strategy Northern Ireland', Northern Ireland Environment and Heritage Service.

Office of the Deputy Prime Minister (2004) 'Survey of arisings and use of construction, demolition and excavation waste as aggregate in England 2003', 04PD02558, ODPM, London.

Patel, N. M. (1997) 'Municipal solid waste management in IEA member countries', Task 23 report, International Energy Agency.

Resource Developments Association (1997) 'Systems and markets overview of anaerobic digestion', Washington DC, Resource Developments Association.

SEPA (1999) 'National waste strategy: Scotland', Scottish Environment Protection Agency.

SEPA (2002) [online]. Available from http://www.sepa.org.uk/nws/guidance/dawp.htm
[accessed 21 October 2002].

SEPA (2006), 'Waste data digest 6', Scottish Environment Protection Agency, Edinburgh.

Shimizu, Y., Kato, H. and Schull, W. J. (1990) 'Studies on the mortality of A-bomb survivors', 9, Mortality, 1950–1985: Part 2, Cancer mortality based on the recently revised doses (DS86), *Radiation Research*, 121, pp.120–41.

SITA (2002) 'Energy from waste', SITA [online]. Available from http://www.sitaonline.co.uk/about/downloads/EfW_brochure.pdf, p.5 [accessed 2 August 2002].

Soyez, K., Koller, M. and Thrän, D. (2001) 'Climate and resource management potentials of the mechanical-biological pre-treatment of waste', in *The Sustainable Landfill*, International Waste Management Symposium, Sardinia, vol. 1, pp.386–9.

Sumner, D., Wheldon, T. and Watson, W. (1991) 'Country wide average first year committed effective dose equivalents from the Chernobyl accident', *Radiation Risks*, Tarragon Press.

The Open University (1997) S280 *Science Matters, Nuclear Power*, The Open University.

The Open University (2000) T541 *Managing Waste: A Business Guide*, The Open University.

UNSCEAR (2000) United Nations Scientific Committee on the Effects of Atomic Radiation (UNSCEAR) 2000 Report to the General Assembly, with scientific annexes, Volume I: Sources, Annex B: Exposures from natural radiation sources, Table 31, p.140.

Williams, P. T. (1998) *Waste Treatment and Disposal*, p.265, John Wiley.

ACKNOWLEDGEMENTS

Grateful acknowledgement is made to the following sources for permission to reproduce material within this block.

Figures
Figure 2: Biffa; Figure 7: Bridgwater, A. (1986) 'Refuse composition projects and recycling technology', *Resources and Conservation*, vol. 12. *Figures 9–11:* 'Landfill design, construction and operational practice', Waste Management Paper 26B, DoE, 1997. Crown Copyright material is reproduced under Class Licence Number C01W0000065 with the permission of the Controller of HMSO and the Queen's Printer for Scotland; *Figure 13:* SITA UK; *Figure 26:* Traymaster Ltd; *Figure 27:*

Adapted with permission from On-Farm Composting Handbook (NRAES-54), published by Natural Resource, Agriculture and Engineering Service (NRAES), 152 Riley-Robb Hall, Ithaca NJ 14853-5701, www.nraes.org; *Figure 30:* Soyez, K. *et al.* (2001) *Sardinia International Waste Management Symposium,* CISA; *Figure 35:* © Science Photo Library; *Figures 38 and 41:* Daniel Chiras, 1998; *Figures 42 and 44:* Sumner D. *et al. Radiation risks: an evaluation,* Tarragon Press; *Figure 46:* Uranium Information Centre, Australia; *Figures 47 and 49:* 5th International Conference on High Levels of Natural Radiation, Munich, 2000. With permission of IAEA.

Tables

Tables 7–8: From 'Commercial and industrial waste survey 2002/03', Environment Agency, 2006; *Table 9:* From *Waste Energy 2000,* Defra. Crown Copyright material is reproduced under Class Licence Number C01W0000065 with the permission of the Controller of HMSO and the Queen's Printer for Scotland; *Table 14:* © OECD/IEA, 1997; *Table 19:* Composting Association; *Table 21:* Boulos et al. (2006), *The State of Composting and Biological Waste Treatment in the UK*, The Composting Association; *Table 27: ENDS Report*, 305, Environmental Data Services Ltd.

Every effort has been made to contact copyright owners. If any have been inadvertently overlooked, the publishers will make the necessary arrangements at the earliest opportunity.

INDEX